Learning Recording Engineering

Fundamental Concepts & Operations

Barry R. Hill

Learning Recording Engineering: *Fundamental Concepts & Operations*

Printed in the United States of America

Library of Congress Cataloging-in-Publication Data

ISBN 978-1-60461-033-8

Contents

Understanding the Recording Industry

Engineering Records in the Studio

Understanding and Using the Equipment

What are the CDs for?

The two audio compact discs that come with this book are loaded with examples of miking, processing, mixing, etc. You can play these in either a standard CD player or on your computer, but make sure you use high quality speakers or headphones to listen through. Since the main purpose for this program is learning how to hear technical and artistic issues with recorded music, you need to clearly hear the sound files. Many examples cannot be distinguished unless you have adequate playback hardware and volume. Also keep in mind that it takes practice and experience to train your ears, so at first you may not notice some of the described settings and nuances. Keep at it!

Chapter One

Understanding the Recording Industry:
What is it?

It all begins with a song. Everything in the multi-billion dollar music industry revolves around a song that someone, like you or me, has written. We perform that song. We print it as sheet music. We record it, play it on the radio, and make CDs and digital downloads to sell. We use it in movies, TV, video games, and cell phones. We sell t-shirts for bands that get famous from that song. We even let others play our song by manufacturing instruments that the public can buy and learn to play at home or school. All the money flowing through this industry originates from the creative talents of a songwriter.

We can then suppose that because of this, the most lucrative career in this business would be as a songwriter. That's true to a large extent. If you write a successful song, all the various uses of that song result in money paid back to you in the form of royalties, as long as your contracts are fairly written. However, not all of us are songwriters, and there are enough bad ones out there already. What can you do in the music industry to make a living? Plenty! There's a huge production and support structure for making money with those songs, and lots of opportunities for you to find a career that not only pays the bills, but lets you enjoy going to work each day.

Today's music industry involves people and skills of all types: songwriting, performance, technology and engineering, manufacturing, business, law, and countless other support areas. No matter what your particular interest and area of expertise you can work with music somehow, somewhere.

If your interest is in technology, there are lots of opportunities for individuals knowledgeable and skilled in the use of technology to produce music in all its various forms and formats. This includes pre-recorded music for various DVD formats, compact discs and ringtones, music produced for TV, video, or movies, music and sound for games and websites, and also production of live sound events, including concerts and interactive media presentations.

If you want to be successful in the field of music technology you've got to become fluent in a variety of areas including computers, web technologies, audio equipment and processes, business, and above all, the knowledge and development of musical skills. Too much of today's music suffers from an over-reliance on technology and tricks. Quality music composition and production from an artistic perspective is needed to produce material of lasting enjoyment and use. You don't necessarily need to be a fluent recitalist, but you should be able to talk music-speak and develop a musical ear. This will enable you to work much more effectively with other professionals and earn respect from the musicians working on your projects.

The same goes for people wanting to work on the business side of things. The more you know about music the better you can relate to the product and people you're working with. Ever go into an electronics store, ask a clerk about some audio receiver, and get some completely idiotic babble about how cool it looks and what the extended warrantee costs? Ever go to the record store and ask a clerk about what they know of a certain artist? Wouldn't you want the music publishers who are selling arrangements to your high school choral and band director to actually know something about the music they offer? The more you know, the more you benefit, along with your clients and employers.

You will also discover that along with developing specific job-related skills you must demonstrate a willingness to work, learn, and interact with people. If you have an arrogant, unmotivated attitude your first job may be your last. The music industry is a relatively small one—there's no room for people who spend their efforts trying to prove their stuff. We once hired a couple of horn players for an album overdub session who showed up with white gloves and polished instruments. They played decently, but none of us could put up with their incredible attitude—they never worked there again. Just do your thing, work with people, help others as you  go along, and it will always pay off in the long run. You will never know it all--there's always something you can learn from anybody you run into. Ask intelligent questions and don't bluff your way through life like you're God's gift to recording. Learn how to communicate (written and oral), learn how to get along, and be ready to listen to a wide variety of ideas that may or may not agree with your own. That's what makes things grow and progress—open your minds and enjoy the interaction.

You've got to get out and talk to people. If you sit at home waiting for the phone to ring you'll get nowhere. Networking is the key to this business—the more people who know you, know what you're good at, and enjoy talking and working with you, the more opportunities will open up over time.

I should also address the perception that this is a male-dominated business— female students and their families always ask about this. The answer is yes...and no. It depends on what aspect you get into, but mostly the opportunities are there no matter what you are or where you come from. Some studio situations and live concert jobs, for example, are probably not very hospitable to females, but overall you can find plenty of things to do in this industry. There are many highly successful females in the business, and interestingly enough some of our most successful graduates from the college are females, so don't be discouraged at all. If you want to work badly enough, you'll find your niche.

Music Technology Opportunities

You never know exactly what you'll be doing in five, ten or twenty years. Don't set your sights too narrowly; keep an open mind and learn to take advantage of the unexpected opportunities that come your way. There are many different applications for using technology in producing music. The most obvious is producing albums in a recording studio. Probably ninety-percent of all students who audition for our college's degree program expect to become recording engineers making rock and roll albums. There are two main issues to point out about this expectation. First, there are practically no jobs out there just waiting for you and hoping you'll show up. There are scads of people like yourself who want to record Sting or Madonna. Second, getting into this aspect of the business is very tiring, very trying, and offers very little in the way of reward for a long time—if ever. A few individuals will successfully become big-name engineers in this area, but most people should open their eyes and look to what's happening in the industry these days.

The two main events that are providing opportunities are video-related and mobile applications. Just look at all the TV programming, video production, film, and interactive websites around you. The current growth in media demand for cellphones, iPods, and other portable devices is meteoric. And it just keeps growing and growing. All this, my friends, requires lots of audio production, which means lots of jobs for you. This may mean sitting in a small room working on a computer workstation synchronizing screeching tires to BMW commercials or working in a project studio developing sound snippets for the latest X-Box release—that's where the money is. It's a visual, mobile media world, and anything with video automatically brings audio along for the ride. Seen any silent films lately?

There's lots of talk about some pretty big studios closing shop around the country. Does this mean the recording industry is dying? Hardly. Not all of these shutdowns are due to lack of business, and as we speak there are other pretty big studios being opened regularly. Much of today's production, though, requires smaller facilities that can fit into your office. There is lots of audio engineering required these days—you simply have to look in different places to find it. Our graduates come back and tell us their stories—on the road with touring shows, managing a band, installing home theater systems, working with theater productions, producing independent films, going to law school, running audio for the circus (!), producing tracks for Guitar Hero, owning their own studio, and yes, even making some albums here and there.

So keep your options open. You can do several things for now—keep reading this book to learn more about fundamental studio recording concepts, which are valid for all the production needs in these various fields. Read industry magazines such as Billboard and Mix to keep up with where things are heading. The more knowledgeable you are about the real world the better you can prepare and tailor your skills and background.

Music Business Opportunities

Technology-related work is only a small slice of the overall music industry. No matter what interests you in life, you can probably find a job doing that in some aspect of the music biz.

Think about the many types of jobs you would find in any industry: executives, managers, salespeople, attorneys, marketing execs, programmers, writers, graphic artists, editors, design engineers, the list keeps going. What this means to you is that you can follow your parents' wish to become a lawyer (only if you really want to) and spend your days negotiating contracts in the biz, rather than editing commas in shipping contracts with a tire company. Here is a short list to give you some ideas:

- Design, manufacture, and sales of musical instruments
- Design, manufacture, and sales of recording and PA equipment
- Editing, printing, and sales of sheet music, books, scores
- Management and operation of record companies

4

- Management and operation of publishing companies
- Management and operation of radio stations
- Computer software development and sales
- Legal counsel (copyrights, recording contracts, publishing contracts)
- Non-profit performance institutions (orchestras, opera houses)
- Archival institutions (music preservation)
- Entertainment publishers (magazines)
- and lots, lots more…

What about performers?

Some of you really, really want to play, and so the often-asked question is "so what can I do as a player?" The answer is not so simple, unfortunately. There are few positions available for full-time players, whether you're interested in an orchestra seat or laying tracks as a studio musician. The competition is absolutely fierce, and even the top players have a very difficult time finding work. I don't want to discourage the better musicians out there who are in fact good enough to play for a living, but you should know the limitations and obstacles and plan accordingly. Planning means you can still find work in the music business and play on the side. It's better to sell guitars than French fries, right?

Playing jobs can include:

- Studio musicians / vocalists
- Live concert musicians / vocalists
- Orchestras, chamber groups, etc.
- Broadway and other theatrical productions
- Regional gig player (plays on traveling shows, concerts, special events)

Some musicians these days are selling their wares by self-producing recordings of samples, segments, or entire songs for media producers—people making commercials, films, etc. This can be done at home or in a small project studio for those who are tech-savvy. It pays to develop skills besides scales and rudiments. Traditionally, many performers supplement their income by teaching private lessons at a local school or music store. You can make a decent living doing this, but it takes time to build up your student roster and get your name on the list for gigs as they come up. Talk to professional players in your area and get their story—see if it's something you want to pursue. You don't want to give up your dream as a musician, but you also need to understand the reality of what's feasible and the route required to get there.

What's this book about?

This text and accompanying compact discs are primarily designed to help you learn how the recording studio works, how recordings are made, and get you started understanding and using the equipment. However, I've included a few chapters at the beginning to provide an overview of the business side of things, at least as it pertains to the making and selling of music and records. You need to know how studio production fits into the big scheme of things. Some of you are interested in selling your own music, selling yourselves as recording artists, or working somewhere in the recording industry. Many of you want to be recording engineers—that's fine, but perhaps we can open a few other doors to expand your options and get you thinking.

The majority of the book focuses on studio production, including learning how recording consoles work, understanding signal flow between microphones and recorders, and getting you to start listening critically to various miking setups, signal processing, and mixing techniques. This book is the basis for a series of college courses that are structured somewhat uniquely. Instead of plunging directly into the theoretical details, which probably mean little to you at this stage, the art of recording music will be demonstrated in context. All the relevant terminology and theory will be covered, but in context of specific applications, not as separate chapter studies. Therefore the first part of the course will break down the stages of multitrack recording.

 In order to familiarize you with studio equipment and operations, mixdown procedures will be discussed and practiced before anything else. This eliminates the pressure of having musicians in the adjacent room waiting for a novice engineer to figure out what they're doing. Mixing involves use of all the equipment located in the control room and facilitates learning signal flow in the studio. It also provides an end-appreciation for how tracking sessions should be handled.

After you've gotten the gist of mixdown and how the gear basically works, we'll go over tracking and overdubbing concepts. Tips on mastering projects will also be provided so you can avoid common problems that trip up even the professionals. Once you understand how the process works and have a functional familiarity with the equipment, we'll go back and explain the specifics in greater detail in the latter chapters of this book. Recording console functions and signal flow, microphone design and technique, multitrack recorder operation, and use of outboard processing will be discussed and demonstrated.

At that time context for this information will have been established, hopefully providing a fuller understanding of the material. This text doesn't pretend to cover great detail of audio theory. There are many fine books available that you can use as references to back up what we discuss here.

It's very important to understand the educational design behind this book and CD. Many people these days think all they have to do is learn how to get signal into Pro Tools and work the plug-ins to be an engineer. Hardly. If you want to be a *real* engineer, one who really understands this stuff and can work like a pro for years to come, then you need to think deeper. The goal is *not* learning how to use a specific recording console or software package. If you learn the standard features, controls, and operations that all recording systems have in common, then you can learn how to use any specific console or DAW (digital audio workstation). Simply look for those standard patterns and see where they are on that particular system. To do this you need to spend adequate time reading the book, listening to the audio examples, and practicing in the studio. If you don't, you are taking shortcuts that will prevent you, or at the very least delay you, from learning the essence of studio production. Not understanding these concepts leads to frustration and a lack of ability to adapt to different or unexpected circumstances. I see it every year with students and can only restate over and over what this paragraph is saying. Trust me!

Is this applicable to your computer-based recording system? Absolutely—the basics never change. If you learn the generic concepts, you can transfer that knowledge to *any* system, whether it be a large format analog console or a software-based ProTools rig. That's what makes this text and CDs effective. The emphasis is on understanding signal routing, the skilled use of microphones, processing, and mixing. The equipment and end product may change over time, but the fundamentals and artistic concepts never do.

What's next?

We'll start by discussing the life-blood of the industry—songs—and how they can make money. You need to know the various income options (licensing) and how songwriters can get their material to the public to generate income (publishing). If you're dead-set on getting into the studio stuff, that's okay. You can read through the studio chapters and check out the CDs, but make sure you review the first few chapters at some point so you know how the recording aspects fit into the overall picture of the industry.

Chapter Two

Understanding the Recording Industry:
Making Money With Your Music

The Big Picture

As we mentioned earlier, the entire music industry runs on one specific fuel—songs. New songs, old songs, good songs, bad songs, they all provide the foundation for the complicated infrastructure of the business of music. The task is to sell these songs as many ways as we can think of. But wait…don't we write songs for the love of the art? To express ourselves? Sure, but while you may get lots of satisfaction from playing your new tune to your girlfriend as she swoons over you, when her father asks about your employment outlook what are you going to say? The fact is that unless we find a way to package and sell your song, it will only be good for impressing your friends. That may be fine for some, but the industry requires that we find people willing to spend money for the right to enjoy these songs. Thus exists the often difficult clash between art and commerce. They don't always easily get along, but we do the best we can, usually doing pretty well in the process.

So, if the goal is to sell songs, how do we do that? The basic need is to get the message out there, to find the right people who have the means and position to do something with them. It also means knowing the various ways people can use and enjoy your songs. This can be difficult for individual songwriters, but there are a few options that can be tried right in your own town:

Market locally

Look for local musicians, writers, publishers, and radio stations interested in your material. Make a demo or album and sell at gigs. Get to know the local music scene.

Market globally

The Internet has generated new opportunities for commerce in general, and music is no exception. You can get the word out for almost no cost—the trick is getting people to find you amongst a vast sea of Internet-promoted music. It's not difficult getting your recordings into the iTunes store, but then you wait for someone to find it and click *buy*. There are artist and repertoire websites that cater to people like you. Sometimes these help, sometimes they don't, but it's worth a try. There's also the tried-and-trusted method of direct marketing by mail to consumers. It's more expensive than using a website, but you target your potential customers directly; many writers do this quite successfully.

Market to publishers and labels

Although it's usually a long shot, mail your material to publishers and record labels that may be interested in your style. This doesn't work well for reasons we'll cover later, but find out which publishers work with your type of material and contact them to see if they'll take a listen to your stuff. Don't waste your money sending demos to companies that don't match your genre, and make sure you include the simple things like contact information (where you can be reached) and other important items—you'd be surprised at how many people don't know how to put together a complete, effective package.

Understand the new paradigms for consuming music

It's not merely about selling albums these days. People listen to music quite differently than they used to. Your song will be downloaded into iPods and cellphones to be listened to while jogging, reading, commuting, or staying awake in Philosophy class. Typically these are not organized by artists' albums, but in personalized playlists as consumers pick and choose the tunes they happen to like.

The problem is that many songwriters know nearly nothing about marketing or how the money-end of the industry works, thus adding to the starving artist pool. You've got to get connected with certain professionals who are in the loop. Most commonly this includes music publishers, entertainment attorneys, labels, agents, etc. The music community is a relatively small one—professionals talk and work together and develop certain trusts and respect for each other. They'll more likely listen to a song when a colleague refers it to them than if a nobody-writer tries to contact them. Legal issues these days also prevent many professionals from taking a chance on hearing unknown songs. Too often a songwriter has tried to sue a famous artist for copyright infringement, trying to prove that the artist had heard their song before releasing a version similar to or exactly like it. This creates a gun-shy environment, so be aware when you try to shop your songs.

In recent times, however, more and more writers are handling their own promotion and publishing (discussed in a moment). These are primarily the successful writers who have already established connections in the industry. They've become better educated in how the business works, probably been burned before by bad or unfair contracts, and want to keep 100% of the income, rather than share it with a publisher. If you're a relatively unknown writer who wants to go big-time, especially for label adoption, then you'd better stick to making a connection with a publisher.

Music Publishing

Music publishing is the process for making material available for public consumption. The songs need to be packaged in some form that is usable (recorded, printed, etc) in a variety of ways. Music publishers handle the marketing of your songs; they have the connections to promote songs and are equipped to handle the administrative duties required for managing songs in their catalog. These tasks can be too difficult and time consuming for many writers, so signing with a publisher is often a good deal.

So, how do publishers help you make money? They promote the song and find people who want to use it for various purposes such as:

- Making and selling recordings (CDs, digital downloads, ringtones)
- Broadcasting (radio play or web streaming)
- Live performance
- Printed sheet music
- Using the song in a movie or TV show
- Using the song in a play or musical
- Video games
- Playing a recording of the song in jukeboxes

The publisher's job is to *license* permission to others for them to use a song, for certain fees. The publisher then splits the income with the writer. These various licenses are what make you money from your songs. The publisher handles all of the work in making the deals and collecting the fees. This is the basic gist of what a publisher does:

- Plug songs to potential users
- License songs once users have been found
- Collect the money
- Split the money with the writer

Once you assign your song to a publisher, they assume all rights to license your song for the various purposes listed earlier. They now *own* your song, meaning they own the copyright to the song and can do anything they wish (subject to the contractual agreement). It may seem difficult to give up your songs like this, but usually the trade-off is worth it. You like to eat, right? You can't feast on manuscripts lying around the house. The writer typically gets at least 50% of the licensing income, sometimes as much as 75%…a whole lot better than what recording artists get, but that's another chapter. By the way, a song can be owned by more than one publisher/writer, such as when a song is co-written or when two writers are with two different publishers. When multiple parties are involved, all contracts between them must stipulate how earnings are to be divided.

Mechanics of Publishing

Music publishers perform a variety of duties with their writers and songs:

- File copyright for songs, issue licenses, collect fees, pay writers and co-publishers.
- Plug songs to get them recorded and otherwise used.
- Help writers improve their songs and perhaps team them with other writers and lyricists.
- Perform title searches to confirm who owns certain songs, register new claims of copyright for new songs, record transfers of copyright ownership (when someone buys the song or catalog from the publisher), and keep records of copyrights owned, extensions, renewals.
- Handle legal issues such as infringement claims, taxes, contracts with writers and licensees.
- Take care of printing, warehousing, inventory, shipping, distribution.
- Acquire new material, generally through two methods—find new writers and songs individually, or purchase another company's catalog. Catalog purchases transfer ownership of the songs to the buyer, who then owns all rights to the songs. This is a common practice in the industry, similar to a corporation purchasing other companies for financial gain.

Types and specialties of publishers

There are several general types of publishers:

- *Major*: These are the biggies that handle all aspects of publishing in-house and are largely self-sufficient. Examples include Warner/Chappell, BMG
- *Affiliate*: Independent publishers who are affiliated with a major, meaning they will contract with a major to handle certain tasks they cannot do in-house, such as printing and distribution.
- *Independent*: A publisher not affiliated with a major company; they're on their own and often outsource various operations. However, this does not mean they are small—they come in all sizes and abilities.
- *Writer/publisher*: A songwriter who handles their own publishing. This is much more common these days, especially with established writers who have an established track record.

Music publishers will usually specialize in certain genres of music, rather than trying to work with everything. Songwriters should understand this and, when searching for an interested publisher, target those that handle the specific style of music they write. A few examples of these categories include mainstream (pop, rock), jazz, religious, educational, choral, children, classical, and other specialty areas.

We mentioned that songs must be produced into some form that can be made available to a consuming public. This most often includes recordings, such as CDs, downloads, and ringtones. These account for the majority of today's publishing business. Printed sheet music and songbooks are another method, but this isn't done as much these days. Rock and pop tunes are difficult to sell on paper because consumers want to hear the sound from the record, not what it sounds like on a piano or trumpet. Tunes that feature a dominant melody are best for print, such as Broadway tunes. There are also fewer families who play traditional musical instruments at home. Once upon a time, singing around the piano was one of the main sources of entertainment for families. Now nearly everybody listens to the radio or their iPods, although an interesting trend has been the development of game-based music such as Guitar Hero. You don't use sheet music, but these games require licensing of recorded songs for folks to jam to on their plastic guitars. So, most of the publishing income these days comes from recording royalties and performance fees (covered soon...keep reading).

Criteria for publishers to accept a new song

What are publishers thinking when they hear your song? Here are some criteria.

- Does the demo hit them? Strike a chord?
- Do they need a song like that?
- Does the composer have a successful track record?
- What label or artist might record this song?
- Is it a really good song?

I know of a major label representative who mentioned having a song sent him by a friend who wanted to know what he thought. The reply was "it's a good song...but it's not a *really* good song." The competition is fierce, to say the least, if you're trying for mainstream recording opportunities. However, here are a few other considerations to keep in mind.

The world needs music for a lot more applications than albums. Think of all the places you hear music—video games, cellphones, instructional videos, commercials, Muzak, websites...the list goes on forever. There are lots of different options for your music, depending on the style of compositions you write. We won't get into this more at this point, but at least start thinking outside the box, learn how the business operates, and see if you can find your own niche.

Starting your own publishing company

If you're interested in starting your own publishing company, whether it's for your own material or to try selling other writers' stuff, there are a few simple steps to follow.

- Come up with a name and affiliate yourself with either ASCAP, BMI, or SESAC (explained later). This gets you on the books for collecting performance license income as well as ensuring you haven't accidentally picked a name that already exists.
- Establish your business locally by running a DBA statement in the local paper. This "doing business as" announcement is standard for any new business. Also check with local authorities for tax information, registration, and other requirements.
- Begin registering songs with the U.S. Copyright Office.
- Register songs with your performing rights society (ASCAP, BMI, SESAC).

Getting officially started is easy and inexpensive...but now you've got to find good material and do something with it to start earning a few coins.

Music Licensing

Now let's take a look at the various ways songs can generate money. There are quite a few, some more lucrative than others, but you can get a sense of how people use songs, therefore generating income for writers, publishers, and other professionals in the industry food chain. Remember this equation: *Use = License = Money*. Repeat it over and over. When someone has a *use* for a song, they must then *license* the right to use that song, which means they must pay *money* to you the owner. Very good, right?

Uses for your song (i.e. money-making options)

There are a variety of ways in which people will want to use your song. Here are the main licensing categories with a brief explanation of what they include. We'll touch on a few of the main ones in the remainder of this chapter.

Type of use	Examples
Broadcast performance	Radio airplay, TV shows, satellite radio, Web streaming
Non-broadcast performance	Live concerts, clubs, schools
Mechanical Licenses	Recordings (CDs, downloaded songs, ringtones, Guitar Hero)
Synchronization Licenses	TV production, movies, videos, video games
Printed editions	Sheet music, songbooks, choral/band
Grand rights	Stage dramas, musicals
Jukeboxes	Jukeboxes (duh)
Foreign rights	Includes all above outside U.S.

Performance income

Anytime someone plays your song in public, a royalty is due to the owner of the song (you and your publisher). This includes live performance by musicians as well as broadcasting a television show with music embedded in the soundtrack. Copyright law provides the song's owner the exclusive right to perform their material. Everyone else must request permission and pay to do so. These performances can either be broadcast or non-broadcast, which simply means whether the music is performed live or via some electronic transmission.

The task is trying to keep up with who is playing your stuff and collecting the fees. Think of the thousands of clubs, concert halls, stadiums, radio and TV stations around the country. How can we track all this ourselves? We can't, but there are organizations that specifically do this called *performing rights organizations*. PROs exist solely to license songs on behalf of their member publishers and writers, collect the fees and distribute payments to their members, and police the users to ensure they are complying. It's important to note that PROs only deal with performance licenses, not anything else listed in the above table. They have nothing to do with recordings, for example. The three PROs in the U.S. are ASCAP, BMI, and SESAC. Writers and publishers can only affiliate with one of these societies.

So, who are the users who pay for performing your songs?

- Radio stations
- Television stations
- Websites
- Digital music programming (XM radio, cable TV streaming)
- Concert halls
- Clubs
- Schools
- Jukebox owners
- Restaurants (well, sort of…long story)
- Girl scout camps (they got sued several years back)

You get the idea—anybody who uses your song for any reason needs to pay up. By the way, if you are a musician playing in clubs or other venues, you will be relieved to know that you are not responsible for paying performance fees—the venue is. I know this was keeping you up nights worrying.

How are performance license fee amounts established?

For live music, the size of the venue, any admissions charges, the weekly budget for live music, and the number of hours music is provided are all examined to determine the fee for a particular location. For radio stations, the size of the station (listening area), type of station, and time of day are all factored into the formula. A small college station will pay far less than a major urban pop station.

For television there is a wide range of fee categories dependent upon the nature of the station, type of use within a particular show or commercial, and time of day. This will give you an idea of the money involved:

Television Category	Range of fees
Primetime broadcast	Very high
Cable channels	Low - medium
PBS	Very low

Having your song included as the main theme for a major TV show can bring you half a million a year, while that same song featured on a PBS broadcast might ring up a few hundred dollars. Background music pays less, of course, but can still add up to hundreds of thousands of dollars over time if it's on prime time TV. You get the idea.

Instead of licensing every individual song that may be played by a particular radio station or television broadcaster, *blanket licenses* are typically used. These cover all songs in the PRO's catalog—keep in mind that separate licenses are required for each PRO, meaning three license fees payable each year for performance rights. There have been attempts by broadcasters for source licensing, which covers individual songs rather than the blanket approach through the PROs. The rationale is that they're not playing all the songs in the PRO catalogs, so why pay more? This is one small part of the ongoing struggle between those who must pay for using music and those who own the music.

Songs vs recordings of those songs

We'll take a quick moment to make the important distinction between the copyrighted *song* and a separately copyrightable *recording* of that song. Performance fees only deal with performances of songs, not recordings. So, when radio stations play the hit singles over the air, they pay the PROs to play the songs embedded in those recordings, but they do not pay the owners of the recordings themselves, who are the record companies.

Quirks in the system

Why haven't radio stations paid the record companies for the right to play their recordings? This is a prime example of what happens when laws are being written. One would think ideally that Congress writes legislation in the best interest of all parties, trying to fairly balance everyone's needs. Not so. Lobbyists are everywhere, pressuring politicians to vote in their favor. Inevitably there will be problems and whacked-out results. In this case, the broadcasters successfully lobbied years ago against having to pay royalties for sound recordings. They simply did not want to pay twice every time they played a song over the air. Thus, the result is that there were no performance rights for sound recordings for years. You could play someone's record anywhere without owing the owner anything. Keep in mind, however, you still owe royalties on the performance of the underlying song embedded in that recording. Make sense? Really? Then you ought to become a copyright attorney.

Having said all that, Congress finally fixed the problem...sort of. They added a license for performance of *digital* sound recordings. This means that any broadcast or live streaming of a digital file requires a performance license, typically paid to an organization called Sound Exchange, who then distributes royalties to record companies and other recording owners (pretty much like a

PRO). So, performing (playing) a sound recording over an analog medium, such as terrestrial radio, does not require a license, but playing a digital recording through a digital medium (such as the radio station's website) does. Go figure, but at least it helps (unless you're on the pay-out end of things).

Another interesting quirk for performance royalties is the exemption granted to movie theaters. This loophole allows them to play the music embedded in movies without *any* performance fees, including the song itself. Therefore theaters do not license with the PROs as television and radio stations must. The only income from music that is used for a movie is from the up-front, negotiated synchronization fee before production—a one-time shot. The one redeeming factor is that having your music in a movie provides lots of great exposure, so hopefully that should translate into CD sales and other types of revenue.

Making a recording of someone's song

Mechanical license is an arcane term from copyright law that simply means permission to make and sell a recording of someone's song. When you record that song, you're making a mechanical, physical copy of that song (this holds true even for digital-only copies that reside on a computer). One of the exclusive rights for a song's copyright owner is the right to make a recording. All others must get permission and pay a fee. In this case, however, getting permission is somewhat different. Here's why.

A song's copyright owner has the exclusive right to make the first recording of that song—no one else can do so without specific permission. However, once a commercial recording has been made public, *anyone* can make a recording of that song and sell them. You don't have to ask permission, but you do have to pay a fee. There are two ways of handling this:

- *Compulsory mechanical license.* U.S. Copyright Law has established a fee structure for what is termed *compulsory licenses*, meaning the copyright owner is compelled to give permission for others to use their work. Users simply calculate the number of copies they will make, duration of each selection they are including on the recording, and multiply this with the current *statutory rate* set by the copyright office. Currently that rate is 9.1 cents per song per record copy distributed (for songs less than five minutes each). So, if an album has ten songs, each song less than five minutes in duration, the record company would pay 91 cents per record distributed. If they manufacture 100,000 albums, this would total $91,000 paid to the publisher (which is then shared with the writer).

- *Negotiated mechanical license.* You (the record company) can negotiate directly with the publishers for what is termed a *reduced rate*, meaning a rate lower than the statutory rate set by the government. All major labels operate this way. Publishers usually agree to the reduced rate for major labels because they figure those album releases will result in lots of sales. If you run a small, local label no one has ever heard of, you might not be able to negotiate a reduced rate, so you would pay the statutory fees.

Do you have to deal with every publisher involved in the songs you're recording? Thankfully, no, if you're going the statutory route. Most publishers outsource these license issues to a third-party organization known as the Harry Fox Agency. Harry provides the service of administering mechanical licenses and payments between users and publishers for a small fee. This makes it very easy to figure what you owe and to whom—you simply calculate the total mechanicals due for your project, inform Harry of your plans, who will then approve and issue the individual licenses for each work (song), and then you pay Harry. Mechanicals are due on total units manufactured, not only those actually sold. This is an important distinction, especially considering that many albums get returned from the stores back to the record companies when they don't sell.

Including someone's song in a TV show or movie

Synchronization licenses refer to embedding copyrighted music in a video-based production, such as a TV show, movie, video, or videogame. Thus, the music is *synchronized* to the video source. This is different from the performance licenses due when TV stations broadcast a show with your music in it—every time the show airs the broadcaster owes performance fees to the PROs. However, for the producer to include your music in that show initially, they must obtain permission from the copyright owner. Thus, there is a distinction between fees required to *play* a song included in a show and the fee required to *include* that song in the show to begin with. This is usually a one-time fee negotiated directly between the copyright owner and the production company who wants to use it.

If you're keeping score, you'll notice that the songwriter/publisher is now collecting income in two ways from synchronized productions—the initial sync fee for including their music as well as the residual payments for performing (broadcasting) the show. With the realization that some residuals can provide potentially large sums of money over time, the owner will often offer the one-time sync fee for a reduced amount to ensure the producers will indeed use it. For example, if a movie producer wants to use a song of yours in a major film, the income options can increase as follows:

- The initial one-time sync fee
- Recurring performance fees if/when movie is aired on TV

- Recurring royalties for home video distribution
- Album sales if the song is released on a movie soundtrack
- Performance fees from radio stations playing that hit song
- Additional mechanicals for other recordings of the song
- Other uses as listed later in this chapter

Synchronization fees can vary significantly, depending on the use. Some of the criteria include:

- How much (percentage) of the song is used
- How prominent the song is in the production (feature vs background)
- Scale of the production (major film, PBS special, local vs national TV commercial)

For example, using a song as background in a low-budget video might only cost a few hundred dollars (if that), but background for a TV show might run a few thousand dollars. A feature theme song in a major film release might fetch tens of thousands of dollars, whereas a national commercial can command up to a quarter-million dollars or more per year.

Using an original recording that belongs to somebody else

Now, you've noticed TV commercials that feature a hit song from the radio that everybody recognizes. Often this isn't merely another recording of that song, but the exact same recording from the album. This provides lots of marketing power, but also incurs an additional cost to the producers. If you want to use an original recording of a song, you have to also get permission and pay a fee to the record company. Remember we explained the difference between the *song* and a *recording* of that song? Well, this is a good example. Here are the licenses the producers must get and who they have to pay:

- One-time *synchronization* fee for the song, payable to the publisher who owns the copyright of the *song*.
- *Master use license* fee for the recording, payable to the record company who owns the copyright of the *recording* of the song.

Note that this is necessary not only for TV commercials, but anything you are producing that would include somebody else's recording.

Digital & Internet Licenses

The advent of digital technologies has introduced many opportunities, options, and headaches for music licensing. These new uses don't always fit neatly into existing licensing and copyright practices, with the result that we now have a maze of complex, difficult to understand procedures, fees, and laws. Here are some of the basic applications and principles to keep in mind regarding uses of copyrighted music in digital formats. You should investigate more in-depth resources, however, since this cannot possibly cover all the issues and ramifications.

Licenses for digital uses of *songs*

- Digital performance (webcasting, streaming, digital radio, cable TV streaming). This provides for the performance (playback) of a digital sound file, but the user does not get a copy of the song on their own system.
- Making digital copies, including downloads and ringtones. These require a mechanical license (remember these?) where permission is automatically given in exchange for payment of a set fee.
- On-demand streaming. This is where the user can select what they want to listen to. These must be negotiated separately to get permission and rates from each song owner.

Licenses for digital uses of *sound recordings*

- For services that provide performance of digital sound recordings, where the user cannot select specific songs, copyright law provides a statutory license so the provider does not have to ask permission, but has to pay the set fee. This includes streaming webcasting, cable/satellite TV digital music streaming, and satellite radio (XM, Sirius). These fee are paid to Sound Exchange who then distributes royalties to the owners of the recordings (record labels).
- If a ringtone is an actual copy of an original recording, permission must be obtained from the record label who owns the recording. This is in addition to requiring a mechanical license payable to the song owner for the use of the song.

Complicated? Yes, and this is the simplified version. Try to remember that anytime someone who wants to use a song and/or an original recording of that song must pay two separate licenses, one to the song publisher, the other to the record label. Digital technologies have complicated the licensing network quite a bit, which is why there will always be jobs available for intellectual property rights attorneys (that would make your mom or dad happy, yes?).

Other Licenses

There are several other licensing options for copyrighted music, but we'll only briefly explain a couple and list a few others. By now you should have a good idea of what licensing means and how it generates income for the publisher and songwriter. Some of these can be quite lucrative, others may never apply to many situations. The industry is always looking for new licensing opportunities, such as ringtones, mobile applications, and Rock Band, trying to maximize earnings from copyrightable property such as music.

Print

This category primarily refers to sheet music and song folios (those "Best Love Songs of the 80's" books), but also includes printed choral, band, and orchestral works. The publisher of the music will contract with a print publisher for a limited period of time, usually 3-5 years, getting about 10% retail price for arrangements, 20% retail for sheet music, and less for folios due to lower total price per song in a book. There are other factors, but typically the income from printed editions is limited. Something to keep in mind is that the folks who produce music arrangements for church choirs and school bands rely almost exclusively on sales of these printed materials to make a living. After all, they can't really sell records of these tunes and make money, can they? So, next time you or your teachers begin photocopying parts for rehearsals, think twice and wonder what it would be like without any new music to play.

Sampling

The introduction and popularity of digital sound samplers in the 80s led to a new concept in using sound recordings. Samplers are designed to record a short excerpt (a sample) from a sound recording which can then be used in another recording being produced. This has been especially popular in hip hop and urban music. The issue is that these samples belong to someone else—the record company that owns the recording. Using these without permission is illegal and unethical, so one needs to obtain a license specifically for sampling someone's sound recording for use in another work. Depending on the material sampled, permission (fee) might also be necessary from the publisher who owns the song underlying the recording. Fees are negotiated individually and can be derived from one or all of the following ways:

- One-time fee
- Percentage of income from sale of the new recording
- Percentage of ownership of the new recording's copyright

events and progress react to cause a radical shift in how things are done. For example, look back at historical events that fundamentally changed the paradigm of how things were done and thought of: the automobile, radio, print, factory automation, and so on.

Now apply this to the record business. Can we develop a better model for getting quality product to the masses? Music websites have proliferated as tools for independent promotion. iTunes is accessible to anyone who wants to post and sell their product. The problem with these is filtering—how to narrow the options for the end consumer. Whereas the majors release a few hundred singles a year, the vast number of individuals who can post their music to a website can range into the many thousands and beyond. Who in their right mind can sift through all this stuff? Remember, the general public buys music they hear on the radio and see on MTV. How will they get the word and become interested? At least the labels perform the handy task of filtering out most (certainly not all) the garbage, providing a short list for us to choose from. Can this in fact be accomplished without them, or with a different concept of labels? What other means do people use to find new songs? Now ringtones are released *before* the record. People hear new (and old) songs on their favorite TV shows or in their video games. My family has X-Box sports games that are loaded with current tunes playing on the radio—that's how my son has discovered many of the songs he listens to and enjoys. Some artists offer raw tracks from their albums for consumers to mix on their home recording systems. Lots of other creative ideas are being tried. The bottom line is that the majors are scrambling to reorganize and re-tool their operations to meet this new paradigm, and indies are in good position to take advantage of it simply because they are generally smaller and more flexible to move quickly.

These are the issues for you to be thinking about as you get started in this business. You can become a worker-bee in the existing system, which is perfectly fine, or you can crank up the creativity and develop a unique niche for yourself, perhaps developing a new method that can turn the industry toward a different direction. We don't have to follow the leader all the time. Somebody has to come up with new ways of doing things—might as well be you. Why not?

**This is the end of side one.
Turn the tape over now to listen to side two.**

Chapter Four

Engineering Records in the Studio:
The Music Production Process

Now that you have a sense of how the recording business works, let's dive into the studio to see how records are actually made. This chapter will present an outline of the process, equipment, and personnel that are involved in music production. Remember, everything we discuss not only applies to making commercial records, but to any kind of audio production. The basics remain the same...always.

Music Technology Facilities

Recording studios require varying degrees and types of specialized construction, design, and equipment. Facilities for producing audio range widely from multi-million dollar complexes to single-room studios in a person's basement. The larger rooms offer the best equipment and acoustic environments for high-end album projects. Many of these feature studio rooms large enough to accommodate an entire orchestra for recording film soundtracks. These rooms are expensive to build due to the extensive acoustic design and construction involved. The vast majority of music production today comes out of smaller facilities, traditionally known as project studios. Usually these studios are geared toward specific types of projects such as music composition for TV and video, voice-over for radio and TV, album production for local talent, audio production for video games and mobile applications, and others. With the relatively low cost of professional-quality equipment, nearly anyone can set up a home project studio and break into some angle of the business.

Though the overall range of available equipment capability and cost is vast, basic principles of sound, music, acoustics, and computers remain constant no matter what the environment. Let me say that again—the basics of engineering *never* change, no matter what gear you are using. Once you understand basic concepts of audio recording, you can adapt to more complex facilities as well as various types of production. The key is learning fundamental theory and operation—you can figure out the specifics as you go along. This book is designed to provide you with the basic understanding of what all this stuff means—it won't make you a great engineer. That comes over time, depending on your particular goals and motivation.

Music Technology Facilities: What's inside?

Most recording studios are divided into two basic areas: the *control room* and the performance *tracking* room. The control room is where the console, recorders, and outboard processing gear are located. This room is acoustically isolated from the tracking room where the musicians and microphones are located. Some studios offer several rooms for performance, possibly including a large main room along with smaller *isolation booths* proportioned for a single singer or instrumentalist.

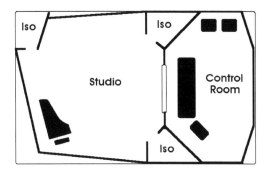

Music Technology Facilities: Who works there?

There are several job functions that must be performed in a studio facility and during recording sessions. Depending upon the size of the company, each of these may fall into separate departments, or they may all be handled by one or two individuals.

Manager

All businesses require someone proficient at marketing, bookkeeping, and publicity to keep the operations going. These business managers ensure that sessions are continually scheduled to keep the studios active, and, of course, keep revenue coming in.

Chief Engineer

Most studios have at least one chief engineer who handles most of the sessions. However, record companies and clients will often bring in their own engineers, many of whom are independent and do not work for a particular studio. Many recording engineers also specialize in either *tracking* or *mixing*. Tracking engineers get the sounds and individual tracks recorded as the producer wants.

Mix engineers blend these tracks into a final product consistent with the producer's vision and goals. This may or may not occur at the same facility.

Assistant Engineer

Often assistants are available (often in the form of school *interns*) who help out before, during, and after sessions in any possible manner. This could include setting up for a session, repositioning microphones, getting coffee and lunch for the crew, cleaning up afterwards, and polishing the floors during off-hours. This is most often the point of entry for new engineers into the music industry. Sometimes these young engineers get paid, many times not. One prominent studio in Los Angeles selects assistants for a one year probation period. They won't actually engineer any sessions during that time, but they will learn the studio operation inside and out. Along with becoming familiar with the studio, the assistants must prove they have the desire and motivation to be successful no matter what. Endurance and a tough skin are useful assets in this business.

Maintenance Engineer

The use of maintenance engineers is required when technical problems or routine maintenance is beyond the capabilities or duties of the recording engineers. These individuals, if located in the right area and have a good reputation, can make a living doing this type of work. On the other hand, if you own your studio and something breaks, it's far cheaper for you to know how to fix it than to call a maintenance expert, especially if you don't live near large markets such as Nashville and New York. These days, though, with the shift toward digital devices there is much less gear that needs fixing—you usually just throw much of this stuff away when it stops working as it's too expensive to send it off for repair. Changing times.

Mastering Engineer

Most often mastering is performed at a separate facility other than the studio. Sometimes this occurs at the manufacturing company that will manufacture the final product, but usually higher-level projects will involve the services of a dedicated professional. The mastering engineer ensures that the final stereo master will work on the destination medium and usually knows how to make small tweaks that can significantly enhance the recording. Sometimes these individuals are quite adept at wrecking carefully produced projects, but there *are* quality engineers out there. Chapter six, *Editing and Mastering*, contains lots of suggestions and warnings for preparing your project for final manufacturing.

Producer

Producers are usually not on staff at studios. They are hired independently by record companies or clients for each project. They are the creative directors for the project, and are responsible not only for controlling artistic direction of the recording, but also managing the business affairs for the project, such as booking studios, musicians, and ensuring the project remains under budget. You will not find a classified job ad for producers in the newspaper; they usually develop from engineers and musicians who are involved in recording music and begin making their own attempts to produce projects. As they refine their own style and sound, they get connected with bands and clients whose particular projects match their abilities and interests.

Studio Musicians

These individuals work free-lance much like producers. A successful studio musician is highly skilled in a wide variety of musical styles, can sight-read on demand, never requires more than one or two takes to record a part correctly, and is much more highly polished than most musicians who only play live shows. You have to witness a professional session to understand the significance. Once in a great while we would be forced to allow an artist's own road musician to play on a session. If this individual did not have lots of studio experience, we could automatically count on the fact that each tune we cut would take three times as long. The reason is that studio musicians are very, very tight with their playing, and they know how the process works. If a pro ever flubbed a note or something, we would finish the take, then rewind immediately back to that spot and punch in (re-record) just that note or phrase. Few words would be required—it was just routine. With the other players, we would have many problems to correct, then have to talk them through each step of the procedure…and hope they would get it right the next time or we'd start all over. Unless you live in a major music region the chances for making a living doing studio work is slim to nonexistent. In the major markets the competition is stiff, but the industry will always need highly skilled players.

How do we make recordings?

There are two main approaches to recording a project.

Live recording

The entire group can be recorded at one time, either straight to a two-track recorder or multitrack recorder. A live-to-two recording is the simplest and most natural of these methods. Two or more microphones are mixed into a stereo image and recorded straight to CDR, flash recorder, or a computer file. The goal is to capture the performance as faithfully as possible and use the natural acoustics of the hall instead of artificial processing devices. The use of a multitrack recorder, including computer-based systems such as Pro Tools, provides opportunity to remix the different microphone signals later, even replacing certain parts and adding artificial processing to replace undesirable acoustics of the recording environment.

Multitrack recording

This is the most common approach for album production. Multitrack recorders can store individual tracks (musical parts) separately, allowing the engineer to work on each part as needed. The musicians can either play all at once, recording their individual instruments onto separate tracks, or they can play one or more at a time. As each part is being recorded, the musician can listen to the previously recorded tracks so they can hear the timing, intonation, and other musical elements of the song. If a musician makes a mistake, the others can go take a break while that one part is corrected.

The technology that allows the recorder to play back recorded parts while recording new parts in sync was developed by Les Paul and Ampex in 1955, and it completely revolutionized the recording industry. Before this, albums were either recorded live with the entire group, or "multitracked" by copying the recording to another recorder, adding another live take from the mics in the process. Just as the earliest motion pictures were nothing but a stationary movie camera filming a play on stage, it took some time for engineers to comprehend the new opportunities made possible with the multitrack recording system.

There are several stages in the development of a multitrack recording project:

Pre-session planning

Before anybody shows up at the studio, lots of planning needs to be done. Since there's usually a record producer in charge of the project, they will contact the studio and begin making arrangements for studio time, equipment, and personnel. The producer will also work ahead on the music, making sure the songs are appropriate and arranged for the artist. Any rehearsals should be done before showing up at the studio—most amateur groups waste all their money by ignoring this critical principle. They don't know what they're playing, so they spend $25-$200 an hour in studio time to figure their songs out.

We once had a local group who only had about $800 to spend on a demo for four songs. At $100 per hour for studio time, we warned them that they only had about four hours to track all the songs, since we wanted to save about half the time for mixing. Since that included getting initial sounds on their instruments,

what's already been recorded, what's currently being recorded, as well as their own playing at that moment. Headphones are used so the playback doesn't leak too much into live mics in the studio, which would be a problem if speakers were used in the room.

The system consists of the sub-mix created on the console or recording system, which is sent to a power amplifier, then on to the individual headphone jacks in the studio. The power amplifier is required to increase the signal level enough to power headphones, and the headphones are for, well...you figure it out.

Monitor System - Control Room

Aside from the original signals coming from microphones and routed to the multitrack recorders, you have to take a copy of these so you can hear them in the monitor speakers. This is called a monitor mix, and it allows the engineer and producer to listen to what's being recorded and make judgments as to what's needed.

This system requires a sub-mix created on the console (a separate mix from the cue mix), a power amplifier to increase the signal level enough to power the speakers, and the monitor speakers themselves. Not to be overlooked is the invisible parameter of the control room acoustics, which can drastically alter the sound from what's actually being recorded. I was paid once to consult at a local studio where the owners couldn't figure out why their sound was so bad. Didn't take long...one look at their cheap walls and the small dimensions of the square room that featured no treatments whatsoever, and it was pretty clear what the trouble was. Wonder if they ever fixed it...

Quality Factors in Recording Production

The Musicians

There are many factors that determine how well your recording will turn out. The most important rule to remember is the ever-pertinent GIGO principle—Garbage In = Garbage Out. If the musicians cannot play well, if they have mediocre quality instruments, and if they are not comfortable in the studio, then there is no chance you will get a decent recording, much less a hit record.

The best studio musicians are virtuosic performers on their instrument, they are well-versed in a wide variety of musical styles, and can sight-read and hear anything you throw at them. There is a reason why you see the same names on the CDs you buy—the majority of musicians just cannot capture in a recording the essence of the music, which is the fundamental requirement for a successful project. We always used hand-picked studio musicians for all our album and commercial projects. On the rare occasion when the client ignored our advice and brought their own bass player in (or worse, their own drummer), we could hardly get through the session. The new musician, even though they may have been playing live on the road for decades, had no idea how to function in a recording session. They just didn't know the routine and operation of getting tracks down and fixing spots. Their lack of finesse on the instrument really came to light also as they could not play exactly in time, in tune, every time like the other players. It was an embarrassment for them as well as for us, and made for long-running sessions which translated into tension and higher production costs.

One time years ago I agreed to help with a local band demo. The drummer showed up with a cheap kit—no big surprise, I suppose. Then I noticed the layers and layers of masking and duct tape all over the drum heads. Those drums were so taped down and muffled he might as well have tapped #2 lead pencils on a coffee table. After several rounds of stripping layers away (and testing his patience since he was convinced they were needed to minimize that awful ringing effect...) we finally compromised, and the result was a mediocre sound on tape. The point is that the musicians must be skilled at getting the best possible sound out of their instrument. Drummers should know how to set up and tune their drums—don't take this for granted, few ever truly understand the concept. I had another drummer show up for a session with a very high-quality kit. We really looked forward to getting sounds on tape because it was a great band and they owned top-notch equipment. We threaded tape on the machine and began working on setting levels, only to hear a pop...pop...pop, where there should have been this great humongous "thoom". The guy had no idea how to tune his drums, nor did he have decent playing technique. The entire album suffered from a lack of drive and energy that should have been supplied by a strong drummer with solid sounds.

A third consideration along these lines is making sure the musicians are comfortable in the studio. Lots of factors affect this: lighting, where they're located in the room relative to the others, a decent headphone mix, how the engineer treats them, how many cabbies ran them down on the way in. If you want a quality recording that captures the magic of the song, pay more attention to these details than you do to the actual recording. Pristine engineering cannot replace an unemotional track.

The Facilities

From the studio perspective, there are many technical factors that affect your recording quality. Acoustics of the studio and control room, which is determined by the size, shape, and acoustic treatment of the rooms, is the invisible parameter that absolutely makes or breaks a project. Too many facility owners leave this to chance because they don't understand it. While the basic principles are not beyond the grasp of most engineers, proper design implementation is best done when completed in consultation with an acoustician who specializes in studio design.

In terms of equipment, there's never been a better time to purchase professional-quality recording equipment at very reasonable costs. Nearly everything on the market, most of it digital, provides the capability of making a decent sounding recording. As long as you maintain your gear you should have no excuse from a technical standpoint. The golden rule is to keep your equipment cool and clean. If you are using reel-to-reel tape machines, clean the heads and tape path regularly—"regularly" being defined as every day, more often during longer sessions. During one of my stints as a piano session player I walked into the control room to listen to the playback. It lacked high end, presence, and life in general—one look around explained why. The studio was not well-kept, was not very clean, and they started smoking as they listened. It's kinda pointless to spend a gagillion dollars on gear only to ruin it all through bad habits.

You also need to learn your gear. Spend a lot of time recording signals and trying various recording levels, EQ settings, and processing controls. Know where the limits are, what makes things sound different ways, how to get the most out of every device or software application. You also must know exactly how everything is connected so that when something goes wrong you can quickly troubleshoot and get things up and running. During a session, everything hinges on maintaining a positive, flowing vibe for the artist and musicians. A bad cable or connection can ruin this if not handled efficiently.

The Human Touch

The last point we'll make here is that a good set of musical and critical ears goes a long way. There are many technicians who learn the plumbing of getting signals from microphones to the recorder, but fewer individuals who have developed a true artistic, musical sense of what they are trying to achieve. This book can provide an introduction to the plumbing concepts while touching on the human issues such as musicianship and people relations, but you've got to develop your own ears to listen critically and musically. Listen to lots of great CDs of all genres. Have professional engineers point things out during a session you are observing. Purchase one of the ear training packages available that help you hear critical technical issues such as frequencies, distortion, phase, and so forth. It takes a great deal of time, effort, and dedication, but that's how you become an expert in any field. There are no shortcuts...dig in and get started.

Chapter Five

Engineering Records in the Studio: The Mixdown Session

What is a Mixdown?

Mixdown is not the first activity in the recording process, but it's a great place to start because you can learn how to get around the console, use the outboard processors, operate the recorders, and get the overall picture of what you're striving to achieve—all while not having to worry with impatient musicians sitting in the studio waiting for you to figure how to get the mic working. Students in my class are given multitrack files with all the parts already recorded; their mission is to figure out what parts are there and mix them down. So what do we mean by this? During mixdown, you take all the musical parts that you previously recorded on the multitrack recorder and weave them into a seamless fabric of stereo space (or surround, but we'll ignore that for now). The individual tracks are played back through the console where all adjustments are made, such as relative balance, left-right panning, and effects, then this final stereo mix is recorded onto 2-track media such as CDR. Keep in mind that although these chapters describe operations mostly from an analog equipment perspective (to make it easier to follow), these are fundamentals that do indeed apply to computer-based systems. Understand what we're saying here and you'll be able to figure out any other device or system you come across.

Signal Flow for Mixdown

You'll see the term *signal flow* quite often throughout this book. This refers to how the audio signals are routed internally through each device as well as how all devices are connected together. In other words, where does the signal come from, where does it go, how does it get there, and for what functions? Our first application is explaining how the different equipment in the control room factors into creating that final mix from the multitrack.

The main equipment used for a mixdown includes:

- Console
- Multitrack recorder
- Two-track recorder
- Outboard signal processors
- Monitor amplifier and speakers

You guessed it—that's pretty much everything in the room except for the coffee pot. The individual tracks originate at the multitrack recorder. The outputs of this machine are usually permanently connected by cables to the multitrack returns of the console's input channels in numeric order (Multitrack track #1 = Console channel input #1).

The individual signals flow down each input channel and are all routed to the master mix output bus, which is a combining circuit that mixes all the individual tracks together. It is a fader located near the bottom right of the console; its output is usually permanently wired to the inputs of the studio's 2-track recorder(s).

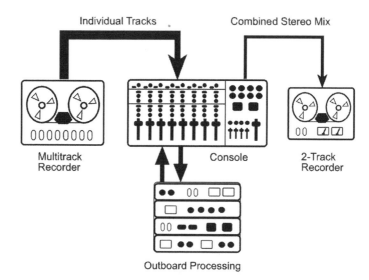

Along the way through the console, you can route any of these signals (musical parts) to your outboard processors. This is how you add reverb, chorus, delay, and other special effects to the song.

What can you do during mixdown?

If you've ever recorded anything in your garage for the first time you've probably wondered what gives professional albums that tight, homogenous sound. The raw tracks of individual instruments usually sound somewhat disjointed and non-cohesive. To pull them together there are several parameters that contribute to how the final stereo mix sounds. Some of them are controlled on the console, some from the outboard processors.

- Tonal adjustments
- Left-right stereo placement
- Relative volume levels between parts (balance)
- Ambiance, sense of space
- Special effects

Controls for these parameters

The diagram on the right is a simplified input channel on a console, which features most of the controls used during mixdown. The following table explains the physical controls that affect the different musical and sonic parameters listed earlier.

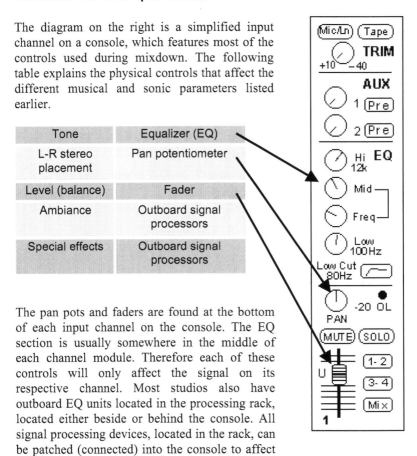

Tone	Equalizer (EQ)
L-R stereo placement	Pan potentiometer
Level (balance)	Fader
Ambiance	Outboard signal processors
Special effects	Outboard signal processors

The pan pots and faders are found at the bottom of each input channel on the console. The EQ section is usually somewhere in the middle of each channel module. Therefore each of these controls will only affect the signal on its respective channel. Most studios also have outboard EQ units located in the processing rack, located either beside or behind the console. All signal processing devices, located in the rack, can be patched (connected) into the console to affect any single channel or group of channels. This is how reverb is added to the entire mix, for example. We'll explain how that is done later in this chapter as we discuss how to fine-tune the mix.

Getting the Equipment Ready

Now that you've got the general idea for what happens during a mix, let's get the gear set up and ready. Remember, there will be differences between various analog and digital devices, but these are the basic concepts that still apply.

It's important to follow these steps in the given order. Some of these will not cause problems if they're out of order, but certain items must be sequenced properly to avoid possible damage or other surprises. Be safe until you know the difference!

The Console

The individual channels (left side of the console)

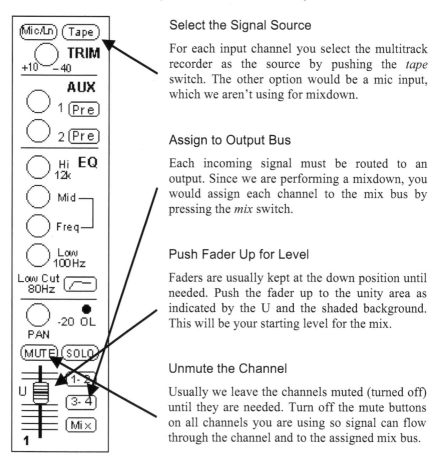

Select the Signal Source

For each input channel you select the multitrack recorder as the source by pushing the *tape* switch. The other option would be a mic input, which we aren't using for mixdown.

Assign to Output Bus

Each incoming signal must be routed to an output. Since we are performing a mixdown, you would assign each channel to the mix bus by pressing the *mix* switch.

Push Fader Up for Level

Faders are usually kept at the down position until needed. Push the fader up to the unity area as indicated by the U and the shaded background. This will be your starting level for the mix.

Unmute the Channel

Usually we leave the channels muted (turned off) until they are needed. Turn off the mute buttons on all channels you are using so signal can flow through the channel and to the assigned mix bus.

The Master Section (right side of the console)

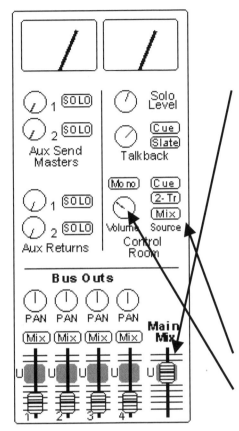

Master Mix Bus Fader

In addition to the individual faders for the channels, there is a master stereo bus fader that controls the overall level of the mix. All individual channels feed into this bus, which in turn feeds the 2-track recorder. Set this fader to optimum level (indicated by the U, zero, or shaded background) and leave it alone throughout the mix. If your levels are too high or too low overall, adjust the individual channels, not this one.

Monitoring Source & Volume

At this point you have signals coming into each input channel, all routed to the main mix bus, and out to the 2-track recorder. This will give you a recorded mix, but it's really nice to also be able to *hear* what's going on. In the main monitor section of the board, select the *mix* source option (as opposed to 2-track or cue), and turn up the volume control next to it. This is strictly your listening volume in the monitors—it does not affect the recorded level to 2-track. Be conservative with your volume levels. Hearing damage will occur if you're not careful, or you may blow something if you press the wrong switch with the volume turned up loud. Until you know what you're doing, keep this low.

Of course, just to keep you guessing, all mixers are not exactly alike. Many of the terms used here may be different from that on your particular model. Some of the functions, such as assigning each channel to the mix bus for mixdown, may be automatic on some boards. Many consoles do not require you to physically select a multitrack tape return for mixing, but this helps you understand the difference between signal sources for a channel. You should understand the process and know exactly where each signal is going so you can adapt to your particular equipment.

The Multitrack Recorder

During mixdown, the multitrack recorder simply plays back the separate tracks recorded during tracking sessions. You need to know where your song files are and be able to find specific locations within each. You should have a *track sheet* for each song, which indicates what's on each track and other helpful information about the recording. Other than that, you're just generally playing and rewinding. Here are the three steps to set it up depending on the type system you're using.

- If you're using a tape-based recorder, clean the tape path on the machine—recording tape sheds its particles, which negatively affects sound quality and machine performance.

  Analog machines need cleaning at every point the tape touches. This includes the heads, rollers, tension arms, and other tape guides.

- Open the file or load the tape and rewind/forward to the desired song.

  Reel-to-reel tapes are always stored without rewinding after playback, referred to as *tails out.* Load the reel on the left, rewind to the beginning, reset your counter and forward to the desired location. For computer files or dedicated hard drive recorders, just open the song file you want to mix.

- For tape recorders, put the machine into *reproduce mode* (sometimes labeled *repro* or *tape* mode).

  This is the highest quality playback mode for analog recorders.

Track sheet for a 24-track studio

The Two-Track Recorder

If you are using a CDR or flash stereo recorder, push the record button once to see your incoming levels, adjust the input level control as needed, then record-play to actually record the mix. For software systems, you will have an input signal indicator in the record window.

If you are mixing internally to an audio file from within your multitrack software such as ProTools, none of this applies. Once you get your mix ready just select "bounce" to create a final stereo file on your hard drive.

Playing back the mix

You have to reselect your monitor source on the console. Remember where you selected the main mix option and turned up the volume to hear your mix? Just push the button that corresponds to your 2-track or CDR recorder—it should already be connected to the console.

A word about levels

When setting levels to tape, there is an optimum range you should be shooting for. If you record too low on analog tape you get lots of tape hiss; too high and you get distortion. If you record too low on digital tape you get lower sound quality, but if you go over the top you get instant, totally nasty distortion. Your goal is to average as close to the top as possible without going over. Experiment with your particular equipment and see how high you can record before distortion begins to kick in.

Getting a Rough Mix

Now that the equipment is configured for mixing, go ahead and set a rough balance of all your tracks. Refer to the track sheet for the particular song you're working with. It shows which instruments are on which tracks, should include any counter numbers to indicate sections of the song, and will also note any comments made during tracking, such as reminders to mute certain tracks at certain times.

Press play on the multitrack and find out what's on it. Start getting a feel for the song and the tracks. Be careful not to run the faders up too high too soon. Keep them around zero, or even bring them back a touch. Levels always seem to creep upward as the mix is built.

Remember, zero on a fader is usually not at the bottom or top, but around 2/3 up the path of the fader. It will be indicated by a number "0" or a shaded area. This is referred to as *unity gain*, where the fader's amplifier is merely passing the signal along without amplifying or attenuating the gain, thereby not introducing extra noise or otherwise degrading the signal.

How should you go about building a mix? Some engineers start with the drums and rhythm section, then add everything else on top. Some start with everything turned on then tweak from there. It's entirely up to you, but it might be advisable to begin with single instruments and sections until you become proficient at hearing things amidst the jumble of the entire band. It's much easier to listen for EQ settings one instrument at a time—just remember that it will sound somewhat different when you blend it with all the other parts.

For now, experiment with different fader settings, then begin placing parts into left-right perspective by turning pan controls. Don't worry so much about EQ at first—just get a decent balance and stereo perspective. Also don't worry about any extraneous noises right before the music tracks start, such as a count-off leading into the song. These will be chopped out of the 2-track after the mix is done (*editing*).

> Audio examples 1 & 2: Editing count-offs

Remember—think musically about what the song is doing. This determines how various tracks are balanced and arranged in relation to one another. Listen to see if the parts fit together musically in terms of rhythm, intonation, harmony, and the overall groove. If a part doesn't seem to quite fit in, either it needs special work with processors or perhaps just needs to be axed from the song altogether.

Go ahead and record this rough mix onto the 2-track and listen back. Your perspective will be different when listening this way because you're not busy thinking about what faders to move during the mix.

> Audio example 3: Rough mix with no panning, levels, EQ, or processing

> Audio example 4: Refined mix with panning, levels, and EQ

> Audio example 5: Refined mix with panning, levels, EQ, and effects

> Audio examples 6, 7, 8: Getting the guitar right in the mix—third time's the charm.

> Audio examples 9, 10, 11: Same for the harmonica.

> Audio examples 12, 13, 14: Again, using a vocal track this time.

> Audio example 15: What's missing in this mix?

Refining the Mix

Refining a mix involves two main steps: finding and rectifying problems with the recorded tracks and creatively enhancing those tracks. Problems should be dealt with first to make room for creative, productive adjustments. Several issues you will often run into are explained here along with possible ways to fix them.

Problems to listen for

The tracks sound muddy and boomy

Explanation:

All acoustic sound sources have a resonant frequency range. This is a region of frequencies that stands out in level from the rest of the sound, resulting in muddying the overall sound. Resonant frequencies are usually in the low-mid range. If not removed, the combined effect from all tracks will result in an overall muddy sounding mix that lacks clarity in the bottom end.

Example:

Muddy, cardboard sound in a kick drum or upright bass.

Solution:

Use a parametric EQ to find the offending frequency range on each affected track.

A parametric EQ provides an extra control that allows sweeping around the frequency spectrum to find specific frequencies to boost or cut, as opposed to a graphic EQ which is set to a fixed frequency. Most recording consoles have some type of parametric EQ. For each band (high, mid, low) there will be two controls: one to boost or cut the signal level, another to select the desired frequency.

How to find the resonance:

Solo the kick drum track by pressing the solo button on its channel. Make sure the overall solo level control, found on the right side of the console, is turned up so you can hear it. Turn on the EQ if your console has an on-switch. Turn up the gain for the low-mid EQ at least 6 dB or so (or around 2-3:00); it should now sound muddier. (*dB* is a unit of audio level measurement.) Now rotate the frequency select control adjacent to it and listen for the changing sound of the frequencies as you move up and down the scale. Turn back and forth until you can distinguish a region which stands out beyond the others and sounds quite muddy. Now reduce the boost control back to a negative number, at least -3dB, maybe as low as -9. The more you cut the more of the overall sound will be taken out, possibly resulting in too thin a sound.

Some parametric EQs provide one additional control that allows you to narrow the region of frequencies being affected (*bandwidth*, or *Q*). By narrowing the bandwidth of frequencies being affected, less of the overall sound will change, allowing you to attenuate (cut) only the offending frequencies.

This same procedure can be used to isolate other EQ problems, such as harsh hi-mid tones.

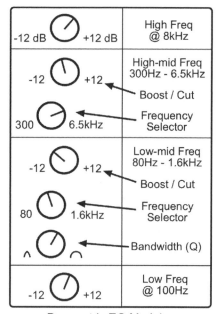

Parametric EQ Module

Audio example 16: Stereo acoustic guitar EQ w/ low-mid cut & upper-mid boost (out/in).

Audio example 17: Bass guitar with low-mids attenuated (out/in).

Audio example 18: Keyboard with low-mids attenuated (in/out). Without the cut, they would interfere with other low-frequency tracks and the mix would be too muddy.

Audio examples 19 & 20: Voice before/after slight low-mid EQ dip to clean it up.

Audio examples 21 & 22: Muddy mixes

I hear other instruments on one track

Explanation:

If more than one instrument is in the studio at one time during a tracking session, individual microphones might pick up other sounds besides the instruments they are assigned to. This is called *leakage*. Most of this should be dealt with during the tracking session by further isolating the sound sources from each other, though some amount of leakage can be reduced during mixdown. Leakage can easily be detected by soloing individual channels and listening, during pauses in that track's part.

Example:

Snare drum sound leaks into the kick drum mic.

Solution:

Insert a *noise gate* into the kick drum channel. A noise gate is a signal processing device that can be used to attenuate or even shut down an audio channel when the signal falls below a certain level, called a *threshold*. It is commonly used to silence background noise on a channel when the main audio signal is not present, such as during pauses between phrases, solos, etc.

Often a drummer plays the snare and kick in an alternating pattern: kick on beats 1&3 and the snare on 2&4. The snare sound will also be lower in level than the kick, since the kick mic is much closer to the kick drum. Therefore, the solution is to set the noise gate so that the kick drum will "open the gate", and the quieter snare drum won't be enough to keep it open, so it effectively shuts the channel down until the next kick.

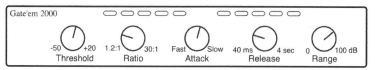

Noise Gate

How to insert the noise gate:

Take a patch cable and, on the main patch bay, connect the kick drum channel *insert send* to the input of any noise gate channel (gates may have one, two, or more individual channels that can be used on different instruments). With another cable connect the noise gate main output to the kick drum channel's *insert return*.

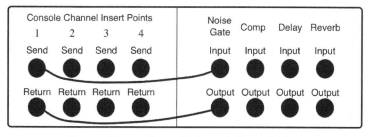

Connecting a noise gate through the patchbay

With this patch in place, the kick drum signal is now coming from the multitrack into the console channel input, breaking away and going to the noise gate, then returning to the same console channel to continue the path through the fader and on to the mix bus.

What is the patchbay? The patchbay is a central switchboard for all equipment in the studio. Instead of physically patching outboard gear into the back of the console, all wiring in and out of all equipment is permanently connected "behind the scenes". To route a signal from the console to an outboard processor, such as a noise gate, simply connect the appropriately labeled jacks on the patchbay. If your studio does not have a patchbay for connecting gear, just use special insert cables and plug directly into your console jacks on the back.

How to set the noise gate:

Gates must be *tweaked* (adjusted) differently for each situation. The two main parameters to concentrate on are the *threshold* and *ratio* controls. Threshold determines *when* the gate will start attenuating the signal (shutting the gate). Any audio signal below the set threshold will be reduced. The ratio determines *how much* the signal will be reduced. A higher ratio will shut the gate down lower, to the point of completely cutting off the signal.

For starters, try a medium-to-low threshold and a high ratio, solo the channel you're working with, and listen. If the gate is cutting out the kick drum sound itself, then you need to raise the threshold and possibly lower the ratio. Experiment to find the appropriate balance. There may not be a perfect fix. Make sure to also work with the attack and release settings as they directly impact how the gate will operate on that particular signal. For starters, keep the attack fast with a medium/long release time, then fine-tune from there.

Audio examples 23 & 24: Snare before/after gating to eliminate the kick leakage.

Audio examples 25 & 26: Kick/snare, first with no gate on the kick, then with kick gated. Listen for how tight and clean the kick sounds with the gate on.

What's all that hum and rumble?

Explanation:

Any continuous background noise that's not part of the music should be reduced as much as possible. This includes guitar amplifier hum, air conditioning rumble, etc. These noises are easily heard and need to be eliminated from the mix. There are various methods for resolving this.

Example #1:

Guitar amplifier hum can be heard when guitarist isn't playing.

Solution:

This is easily solved by inserting a noise gate into the guitar channel in the same manner as for the kick drum described earlier. Simply set the gate threshold just above the level of the amp noise. Make sure that it doesn't chop off any of the guitarist's notes, including the fade out of the last note played.

Example #2:

Air conditioner rumble in the background.

Solution:

Most rumble caused by air systems, traffic outside the studio, and other causes are low frequency sounds. These can usually be reduced by the use of a low-cut filter on the console channel. A low-cut filter is part of the EQ section and cuts all frequencies below a certain, preset frequency. This preset frequency, known as the *cutoff frequency*, is most often somewhere between 75Hz and 100Hz (although some consoles give you a range to select from). Since this region is below most musical instruments it is safe to turn it on, thereby eliminating most low frequency interference. Of course, it shouldn't be used on bass guitars, which go down to 30Hz, kick drums, and other low-frequency instruments.

> Audio example 27: Low-cut filter out/in. Listen for the noise that goes away.

The overall mix levels are difficult to control

Explanation:

When musicians play, their dynamic range usually varies quite a bit between soft and loud passages. Even during a relatively consistent rhythm part, such as from the rhythm guitar, fluctuations in a musician's playing cause significant differences in recording levels. Even when carefully tracked, variations in amplitude levels on some tracks can cause overall mix level problems. Much of this should be handled during the tracking sessions, described in the next chapter. However, the same principles can be applied during mixdown.

Example #1:

The pianist plays a few big, loud chords during a climax of the song which makes the entire mix level too hot at the output bus.

Solution:

There are several possible solutions. The easiest is to simply pull back the piano tracks at this point using the channel faders, if it doesn't affect the overall dynamic push of the song too much, musically speaking. If this doesn't work, then insert a *compressor* for each piano track (if more than one) to control the dynamic range of the piano. A compressor is an automatic volume control—like a cruise control for levels. It reduces the level on audio signals that get too high and that may cause problems for the overall mix or the recording media (causing distortion).

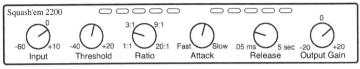

Compressor

Example #2:

The bass guitar continually jumps in and out of the mix because the recording levels are all over the VU meter.

Solution:

Insert a compressor into the bass track to smooth out the variation in levels.

How do you do this?

In the same manner as that done for the noise gate described earlier, patch the channel insert send for the offending track to the input of a compressor through the patchbay. Then patch the output of the compressor back into the insert return for the same channel. Remember each channel of a compressor (as well as a noise gate) only affects the single channel it's inserted into. If you are compressing or gating a stereo pair of tracks (piano, for example) then you must connect a compressor channel for each track, preferably using a stereo compressor which can link the two channels together.

If you don't have a patchbay for your processors, or in case you're wondering how the patchbay magically makes these connections, the following diagram shows exactly what's happening to get the compressor unit (or any other processor) inserted into a specific channel signal.

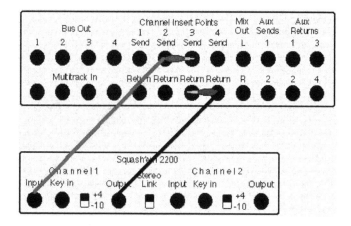

The controls for a compressor are similar to that of the noise gate, but operate in the opposite manner. The *threshold* setting indicates which levels *above* it will be compressed (reduced). Therefore signals hotter than the threshold setting will be compressed. The amount of compression is determined by the *ratio* control. The numeric ratio markings signify the amount of incoming signal vs output signal. In other words, a 3:1 ratio dictates that for every 3dB of input signal, only 1dB of that signal is output from the compressor. Therefore, a higher ratio such as 5:1 will provide a greater amount of compression.

If you only need to knock off a few high peaks, but don't want to affect the entire dynamic range, then set a higher threshold (zero or above) and higher ratio (5:1 or greater). If the overall signal needs to be compressed to tighten the entire range, then set a lower threshold so more of the original signal will be compressed.

Learning compressors and noise gates takes lots of practice and experimentation. Go ahead and play around with the controls to see how these devices affect sounds.

> Audio examples 28 & 29: Acoustic with obvious compression, then a lighter setting.

> Audio examples 30 & 31: Snare without, then with compression.

> Audio examples 32, 33, & 34: Upright bass, distant miked, first with no compression, with slight compression (3:1 ratio, -20 thr) and significant compression (8:1 ratio, -20 thr).

Audio examples 35, 36, & 37: Mix with no compression, mix using Drawmer 1960 tube compressor (-3 thr, -2 GR), then same Drawmer with more compression (-20 thr, -5 GR).

Did you hear something in there?

Explanation:

During tracking it is inevitable that lots of extra sounds will end up on your recorded tracks. Musicians coughing, music stands being hit, cellphones ringing, and clicking drumsticks need to be eliminated. I once tracked an album that ended up being mixed in Nashville by somebody who didn't pay enough attention to this. One of the vocalists coughed during the instrumental introduction—the engineer muted these vocal channels during the mix, but somehow didn't notice they were still being fed to the reverb unit. So, I can pull the CD off my shelf anytime I wish and hear some dude coughing in ReverbLand before he begins to sing.

Solution:

Spend time before the mix session going through the tracks listening for garbage such as this. Erase them while being careful not to erase any of the music parts. During the mix it is advisable to *mute* (turn off the channel) all unused tracks during the song, such as a vocal part during an instrumental solo. Any channels that are not used at all should be kept muted during the mix. Not only will muting silent tracks prevent unwanted noises inadvertently finding their way into the final mix, but it will also reduce noise inherent to electronic devices. If you're using analog tape, each open channel playing back from the recorder contributes 3dB of tape hiss, so for sure mute those unused channels.

Creative Enhancements to the Mix

Once problems have been identified and remedied as best as possible, attention can be focused on constructive elements that creatively enhance the mix. This includes equalization, reverberation, and special effects.

Tonal adjustments

Explanation:

Often different parts need brightening or have too much bass. As opposed to the destructive "fixing" EQ discussed previously where resonant frequencies and other problems are eliminated, constructive EQ application helps mold the tonal characteristics of the mix to the engineer's and producer's taste.

Example #1:

Cymbals need more shimmer and zing on top.

Solution:

Boost high frequency EQ on the cymbal track(s). High frequency EQs are usually set around 8 - 12kHz, which is the upper range of cymbals.

Example #2:

Snare drum needs more snap.

Solution:

Using the parametric EQ, boost the hi-mid EQ and then sweep the frequency selector around to find the crack of the drum sound. Once the desired region is found, boost the EQ to desired taste.

> **Note**: Be careful about boosting too much EQ. Inexperienced engineers generally tend to use too much EQ which results in an unnatural sound. Also, too much boost will increase the overall dynamic level of the signal, which can easily overload the circuits in the console (distortion). Lastly, EQing individual instruments should be performed with the entire mix in mind - don't spend too much time on a single, solo'd track, only to discover that it sounds bad in the entire mix.

Audio example 38: Acoustic guitar before/after EQ.

Audio example 39: Setting the acoustic guitar EQ.

Audio example 40: Brightening the cymbals with hi-freq boost.

Audio example 41: Snare drum before/after EQ adding snap and punch.

Audio example 42: Drum set EQ on individual tracks (out/in).

Audio example 43: Too much hi-EQ on mix.

Audio example 44: Too much hi-EQ boost on cymbals, then reduced to normal.

Ambiance

Explanation:

Since tracks are often close-miked in an acoustically controlled studio, there might be minimal natural reverberation picked up by the mics that provides music with a sense of space. Music needs reverberation to make it sound natural, so often this ambiance must be added in the mix. The engineer can choose the type of reverberation sound (large concert hall vs small jazz club) as well as how to add reverb to each of the tracks. One overall reverb sound can be blended to all tracks, or different reverb *patches* (settings on the reverb devices) can be specified to individual or groups of tracks. A reverb device artificially creates random reflections that simulate how sound waves bounce around in a particular type and size room. Be sure to experiment with the various parameters on the unit—very seldomly will the factory presets work perfectly for each mix situation. These parameters include: changing how long the reverb lasts (*reverb time*), how soon after the initial audio signal the reverb begins to sound (*pre-delay*), how large or small the reverb sounds (hall vs small club), and others.

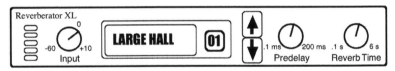

Digital Reverb Unit

How to do it:

Reverb and effects devices are usually not patched into the console the same way as compressors and noise gates, which use the insert sends and returns on individual channels. Reverb devices are instead accessed through the use of sub-mixers in the console called *aux sends* and *returns*. Each channel will have an identical number of auxiliary sends, usually at least three or four. Aux send #1 on all channels will feed a common summing amplifier, called the master aux 1 send, located at the right of the console. The output from this control can be patched into an outboard device such as a reverb unit.

The output of the reverb unit must then be routed back into the console and blended into the overall mix. It does not return back to the individual music channels. The reverb device output can be plugged into an aux return, which is a simple input on the console that directly feeds the mix bus, or it can even be patched into an unused input channel and routed to the mix bus just like the other music tracks. Using an extra input channel gives the engineer all the standard controls: EQ, panning, and fader control over the level. This can be more powerful than the aux returns on some consoles that may not have these features. The result is the same—the reverb'd signal is then blended with the original tracks at the mix bus, giving the perception of "adding reverb" to the sound. Think of this procedure as a loop where your original signal must go out to the effects unit using an aux send, then must return back to the console using an aux return.

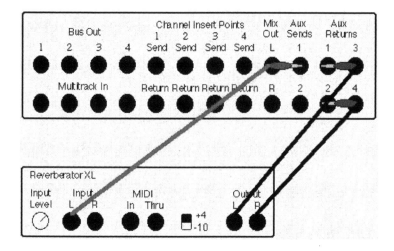

Most reverb units have stereo outputs, but some only have a mono input. If your unit has stereo ins and outs, you can use two aux sends (one for each input) to maintain stereo perspective through the reverb unit. Simply turn up the first aux on tracks which you want panned toward the left; turn up the second aux on tracks which stay in the right perspective. Even better, many consoles have stereo aux sends with pan controls—much easier. Send the left send to the reverb left input, the right send to the reverb right input.

To set all this up, patch the aux send outputs on your patchbay into the inputs of the effects device. Now connect the outputs of the device into two aux return jacks (or empty input channels). Note that some consoles have mono returns, others have stereo returns. If your console has stereo returns, then there will be two jacks on the patchbay for this return, but only one level pot on the board for their combined level. If the console has mono returns, then two returns must be used for each stereo effects device output. Make sure you pan each return left and right so you preserve the stereo signal from the device.

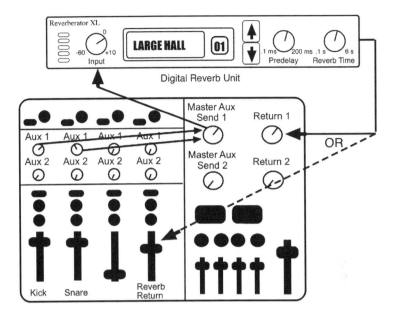

Aux sends from each channel are summed at the master aux send. This is then routed through the patchbay to the input of a processor, such as a reverb unit. The processed output is returned to the console into either an aux return, or into an empty input channel module.

Now turning up aux 1 (or whichever aux you use) on any of the music tracks will send a copy of those tracks to the reverb unit, which then adds reverb to the signals. If a different reverb patch is desired, say for the vocal track, then simply patch a second reverb unit from aux send 2. Route the output from this device into another aux return or unused input channel on the console.

Note: Be careful not to overload the input of the reverb devices by turning up the aux sends too much on too many channels. Watch the input signal indicators on the device to ensure a safe input level.

Audio examples 45-48: No reverb (dry), large hall reverb, small hall, medium room.

Audio example 49: Reverb with distinct echoes

Audio example 50: Gated reverb—listen for how the verb is abruptly cut-off.

One more item for aux sends. It's usually set by default, but you want to send your aux signals post-fader from each channel. Huh? This merely determines where in the channel signal path the aux gets its source—either before or after the channel fader. If you send an aux signal before the channel fader level, then anytime you move the fader up or down it won't affect the aux level leaving that channel. If the aux is after the fader, then moving the fader *does* affect the amount of aux signal going out. For adding reverb and most effects you typically want the aux send to follow the fader level, so set your auxes post-fader. In other words, when you use the fader to turn your vocal up and down during the mix, you want the vocal reverb to adjust with it. In audio example #52, the aux is set to pre-fader. Listen for how the reverb continues after the main channel fader has been attenuated all the way—a cool effect when you want it, but generally not for "normal" reverb stuff.

Audio examples 51 & 52: Setting the aux send post-fader vs pre-fader.

Other special effects enhancements

Example #1:

Make an individual or small group sound like a larger ensemble.

Solution:

The best solution is during tracking. Have the musician or group perform the same part two or more times onto different tracks. The subtle differences from each performance lend the illusion of a larger group.

A mixdown solution is to use an effects device set to *chorus*. Effects devices are capable of providing different types of effects, including reverb. Route the device just like that for reverb described above, but set the unit for a chorus effect. Be sure to experiment with the parameters to tweak the patch for the particular song.

Example #2:

Make an individual instrument sound fuller or fatter.

Solution:

1. Use a short doubling effect with a digital delay unit. A digital delay device takes an incoming signal, holds it for a user-defined amount of time, then outputs the delayed signal. When blended in the mix along with the original

track the difference in time can be either obvious or very subtle, depending on the time delay settings.

For a doubling effect, patch in the device as described for a reverb unit, then try different delay settings to make the sound fatter without creating a distinct echo or delay.

Digital Delay Unit

2. Another option is to set a longer delay time so that the delay *is* audible. An effective method is to pan a rhythm guitar to one side, delay it audibly and pan the delayed signal to the other side. This helps make the guitar track "move" in the mix and livens up the space. Often a delay on the lead vocal can be pushed back into the mix, shrouded in reverb. This brings less attention to the delayed signal itself, while still enhancing the main vocal track.

3. A third possibility for making a track sound fatter, such as a snare drum or bass guitar, is inserting a compressor directly into that track. Compression tends to tighten and fatten a sound, though overdoing it will begin making it sound squashed.

Of course there are countless creative possibilities available to the mix engineer. These basic tools can be applied in any number of ways and combinations; only experimentation will provide a working foundation for what techniques can work in various situations. These are only a few ideas to get started with and should be used as a foundation for developing a musical, critical ear.

Don't forget the simple things! Don't rely too much on signal processing to make the song work. Think musically about the levels, the different parts and how they fit together, and where everything fits into the stereo space you're creating. Think globally before you start reaching for the EQs and patch cables.

> Audio examples 53, 54, & 55: Dry track, adding chorus, flange.

> Audio examples 56 - 58: Reverb with flange, chorus, phaser.

> Audio examples 59 & 60: Mono organ vs stereo organ with chorus.

> Audio examples 61 & 62: Dry track vs adding delay.

> Audio example 63: Vocal without, then with delay.

> Audio example 64: Mix with vocal dry, then with delay.

> Audio example 65: Mix with delay and FX on vocal.

> Audio examples 66 & 67: Snare without, then with compression to fatten and tighten.

Overall things to watch for

Creeping mix levels

Resist pushing faders up repeatedly as the mix develops. If all faders are too high, the mix bus will probably be overloaded and you have no more room to adjust balances. Keep faders conservative—around unity.

Transient levels

Very short, sudden, high amplitude signal levels are called *transients*. These go by quicker than a VU meter or human eye can often see them. The crack of a snare or the attack of a piano or guitar causes transients and they should be controlled, often through light compression during the tracking session. Instead of relying on VU meters, which average out signal level changes, you should also use a peak-reading meter that will display all transients accurately. Transients can cause distortion if severe enough and unresolved, so pay attention.

Hot spots in the mix

Always keep one eye on the mix bus VU level meters to watch for peaking levels. If a section of the song really slams the mix VU needles over to the right, it may overload the 2-track recorder and will cause difficulties when mastering. Find something in the track to pull back at the critical moment, compress an offending track or tracks, or do something to resolve these. They cannot be ignored.

Mono compatibility

Yes, some people just might listen to your album or TV show through a single, mono speaker. Any stereo miking or effects processing may induce certain phase relationships between left and right channels that can cancel out when the mix is played over a mono system. It's really embarrassing to lose your lead vocal due to that cool stereo delay you tried. Always test your mix by pushing the *mono compatibility* switch (available on most consoles).

Control room monitoring volume

DO NOT mix at very loud listening levels. Human ears cannot withstand high sound levels for long periods of time. They will tire over time, distorting what the engineer is hearing, and eventually damage *will* occur. I engineered a session where the producer, a long-time Nashville veteran, needed the volume up so high my ears began distorting after thirty minutes or so. I literally heard distortion and thought at first it must be something overloading on the console or recorder. Nope – everything had been set correctly at the start of the session, so what I was experiencing was my hearing system actually being overdriven, just like a power amplifier that begins clipping. It was an interesting analysis, but not very comforting at the time.

The other problem is that humans hear differently at different volume levels. If a song is mixed at high volume, where the ear more easily hears low and high frequencies, when the song is played back on a small stereo system at home the listener will not experience near as much bass and treble at the lower listening volume. See a reference text for detailed information on the *Fletcher-Munson Curves* which graph this phenomenon.

The solution is to mix around 85dB SPL (sound pressure level). This is a moderately loud setting that provides the best compromise for frequency response (how humans hear low to high frequencies) as well as longevity for hearing clearly and not damaging anything. How loud is 85? Moderately loud. I'm sure that helped. Go buy an inexpensive SPL meter at Radio Shack (about $50). I've also used SPL apps for the iPhone—very handy and inexpensive. Play your CDR at home and in the car at different volume levels to see if your high and low end varies too much.

Cheap EQ fixes

Don't fall into the trap of attempting to salvage dull sounding mixes by cranking up the high EQ on the overall mix. This is often referred to as giving the mix more *air*. Many engineers boost hi end by as much as 6 to 12dB or more; this creates a major problem when mastering for duplication. This boost in signal level, especially at the high end, means that the overall program level must be reduced below maximum available recording levels in order to make sure it will all fit within the specs of a CD. The mastering engineer will have no choice but to either EQ it back to normal, compress the entire program significantly, or more likely reduce the overall program level so that the boosted range will fit. This results in lower level program material, thereby forcing the end listener to crank up the volume more than normal.

Solution? Record tracks correctly to begin with and pay attention to these details along the way.

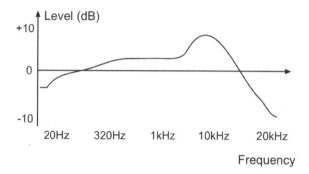

The 10kHz region has been boosted nearly 6dB, way above all other frequency components in the signal. To record and duplicate this, the overall signal must be reduced accordingly so that this peak level can fit within the dynamic range of the media.

Documentation and tape labeling

Just as track sheets document what was recorded on the multitrack, careful notes must be kept for the mixdown sessions. Often several mixes of one song will be performed, and someone will have to find a particular one at a later time or date. Keep a record of what's on the CDR, carefully name all computer files, note counter or index numbers, and indicate any incomplete mixes left on the 2-track as well as which sections of various mix versions of a single song will be spliced together to compile a final mix.

Make absolutely sure that the final, edited 2-track is clearly labeled with all program content, starting times and ID numbers, artist and project information, test tone info, etc. Refer to *Editing & Mastering* for further details. Get into the habit now.

Audio examples 68, 69, & 70: Too much reverb.

Audio example 71: Distorted input on delay unit—level is too high.
Audio example 72: Mix bus is distorted—watch those levels!
Audio example 73: Mono mix.

Audio examples 74 & 75: Out-of-phase mixes, the second was a student mix that went terribly wrong.

Advanced mixing concepts and methods

Now that you've got a little practice with some basic mixing, let's take it a little farther with some overall issues to keep in mind along with some tips and techniques to help fine-tune your mixes.

Overall objectives when mixing

- Attempt to capture the "magic" of what the song means. Don't lose sight of this while playing with all the gear.
- Make it sound like everything's in the same room/space and belongs together.
- Creatively use the sonic space available (stereo field, depth, etc).
- Determine what belongs (or doesn't) in the mix: tracks, specific parts, effects, noise.
- Ensure appropriate recording levels in the console (stereo bus, groups) and at the stereo recorder.

Human hearing subjectivity issues

The human hearing system is not linear and does all kinds of strange things to your audio. You need to be aware of how we perceive sound and what that means for your engineering methods.

We translate sounds into a 3-dimensional space that can be manipulated through our processors and controls.

- Width (left-right pan)
- Height (EQ)
    - High frequencies are perceived as near the top of the sound.
    - Low frequencies are perceived more toward the bottom.

- o No, this does not mean that highs float over top of everything and lows run along the floor...this is simply how our ears perceive sound.
- Depth (EQ, reverb/delay)
  - o Low frequency boost makes a sound seem closer.
  - o Hi frequency boost gives you more targeted localization (position in the stereo field). It also makes it seem closer.
  - o Reverb/delay moves things farther back into the mix.

The objective is to manipulate sounds among these variables to make a clear, coherent mix that's appropriate for the style.

Frequency response

Fletcher-Munson curves: these show us that we do not hear a linear 20-20kHz, but rather that our hearing is very uneven throughout the spectrum. This is what allows us to hear the world around us in a very effective way, but the catch is that this response changes depending on volume. Crank up the volume and we tend to hear more bass and treble. So, if you mix really loud, you'll tend to lose the highs and lows during regular playback at home because you heard more of these frequencies in the control room than were really there.

The solution? Mix around 85 dB SPL, which is a good average volume. Buy an inexpensive SPL meter at Radio Shack or an iPhone app to set you straight.

Stylistic issues

Different mixes for different styles of music. Too many young engineers are stuck on their favorite types of music, but you've got to be at least aware, if not experienced, with how different music is recorded and mixed. Hip hop is very, very different from blues in many ways. I've seen engineers well-versed in one style of music trying to track and mix something completely out of their element. Everybody becomes frustrated, so try to expand your horizons a bit.

Steps, strategies and techniques

Use this list as an outline for preparing and conducting a mix session.

Turn everything on ahead of time so your gear can warm up. Yes, it makes a difference in sound because thermal changes cause slight differences in the values/specs of electronic components.

- Apply compression to this stereo pair of drum tracks and route to the mix bus.
- You can do this with nearly any part of the mix.

The different timbres that result from the uncompressed and compressed stereo group make for a rich, powerful sound. Be aware, though, that with software recording systems you need to worry with latency issues, where the signals being processed with extra stuff get slowed down compared to the unprocessed signals—remember phase? Some systems provide compensation for this, so check with your software manual.

Add a low frequency tone to the kick drum

This adds more "oomph" to the bottom end and is common in hip hop recordings. The idea is to use a tone generator and blend it with the kick track. You only want the tone to come through when the kick hits, then turn off between hits.

- Patch the tone into an empty channel, then insert a noise gate.
- Patch a copy of the kick track to the key in (sidechain) of the gate. A key function is an external "go" switch – when the key input sees a signal, it tells the processor to do its thing. So in this example, when the kick hits, this triggers the gate to open, allowing the tone to be heard. It then closes afterward depending on the gate settings.

You can get creative and apply the same technique with a variety of sources. Use a percussion track to trigger a synth pad to create an interesting rhythmic pattern.

De-ess a vocal track without a de-esser

The consonant "s" often causes a problem we call *sibilance*. It has excessive energy and sizzles above everything else. It can also cause distortion, so you need to get rid of it. Here's how:

- Insert a compressor on the vocal track and set it to key/external mode.
- Feed a copy of this vocal into a separate EQ: boost 4-6k significantly.
- Take this EQ'd signal and patch into the key input of the compressor inserted on the main vocal channel.
- The boosted sibilance frequencies from the external EQ triggers the compressor, thereby reducing sibilance energy without compressing the entire sound. Don't worry, the exaggerated EQ trigger signal is not heard in the mix; it's simply used as a trigger.

Ducking

This is used for radio spots and such where you have a background music bed that needs to lower in volume when the voiceover is speaking. You can do this manually, but why bother when your gear can do it for you?

- Insert a compressor on a music bed being used for your radio ad.
- Take a copy of the voice-over track and key into the music compressor.
- When the voice begins, the compressor automatically reduces the music track, then resumes original volume when the voice track stops.
- Of course this process can be used for more musical situations—be creative.

To help ensure your parts are all working together without sticking out or getting lost, lower your control room monitor level to nearly zero. If anything stands out or disappears you should probably consider adjusting some faders.

Compressing/processing the mix bus (the entire mix)

- Are you sending it to a mastering engineer? Don't do it yourself. Leave it alone.
- Otherwise consider mild compression on the mix bus. Even better, process this afterwards in a software editing program.

Audio example 76: Kick and bass with bussed parallel compression (out/in).

Audio example 77: Just the bussed kick/bass compression.
Audio examples 78 & 79: Same as 77, but first with fast attack on compressor (listen to beginning of each note). Second example begins slow attack, then fast.

Audio example 80: Drum set with parallel compression out/in.

Audio examples 81 & 82: Adding tone to kick, first just the kick with tone out/in, then same with entire drum set.

Audio example 83: Warming a track by running through a tube processor.

Once the mix is done...

When the final mix is recorded on the 2-track, each song must be individually edited and, in the case of an album, often re-sequenced to match the desired order for the record. Basic editing involves chopping any count-offs and other extraneous noise at the beginning of the track, before the music actually starts, as well as deleting excess silence after the song dies away. In the next chapter we'll explain about editing mixes to prepare them for duplication or whatever the end product will be. Read on.

Chapter Six

Engineering Records in the Studio: Editing and Mastering

What is editing & mastering?

Once the final mixing is completed for the entire project, the mixes must be prepared for duplication and distribution. Most editing is performed at the mixing facility for a variety of reasons, generally to get rid of any extraneous noises before and after each song and to insert timed silence between songs. Many times a final mix of an individual song is compiled by editing together various segments of the song from different mixes, choosing the best take for each section of the song. Lastly, the songs are sequenced in the desired order for the album before shipping to the mastering and duplication facility.

A mastering engineer's job is to ensure the stereo master will work when duplicated on compact discs or whatever the delivery medium will be. Mastering a project involves watching for level problems, such as hot spots that may overload (distort), tonal problems (such as too much bass or treble), or even problems such as incomplete takes, noise and spikes in the music, incorrect ordering of songs for the album, and so forth. It's amazing how often mix engineers assemble masters that contain errors. A friend of mine was preparing a master for a Disney soundtrack release, thought he detected something awry, and sure enough found errors in the data codes. The entire production run (about 50,000) was put on hold while they tried to convince the original engineer to prepare another master. A good mastering engineer not only fixes problems, but also enhances the overall sound of the project through careful tweaks here and there. Once these final adjustments are made to the mix master, a new master is created for use in manufacturing the final product.

Editing

During mixing from multitrack the engineer will not bother with various noises before and after the song, such as the introductory count-off leading into the song. Once a satisfactory mix is complete, these intros and endings can be easily cleaned up in software. There is also usually around three or four seconds of silence inserted between songs for an album. For analog 2-track, this means physically cutting the tape right at the beginning and ending of each song, a process explained below. For software, this means chopping the file like a word processor.

step, so these are sent directly to the manufacturing facility. However, even if you don't have the facilities (or money) for proper mastering, you should be aware of the finer points of the mastering process. This will aid you in better preparing your master files so the mastering process becomes merely a refinement, rather than a major overhaul of a badly produced recording.

The main components of the mastering process include various applications of compression, EQ, and other processing. These usually entail very subtle, carefully chosen adjustments, and knowing which steps to take requires long experience and highly developed ears. Many projects are overdone these days, especially with easy access to software processing plugins. Some tweaks are needed to fix problems, such as channel imbalance, erratic frequency response curves (too much or too little high or low end, for example), sibilance, ticks and pops, phase issues, etc. A mastering engineer friend of mine has actually developed a technique to fix phase problems within a single *part* of a mix, something nearly impossible to correct unless the project is completely remixed. Once these are done, you can focus on enhancing the overall sound of the master. These usually center around judicious use of EQ and compression, but there are lots of different types of these processors along with other processing applications that can improve (or destroy) your final mix. Aural exciters generate additional harmonics that add extra zing and brightness to a track. The BBE Sonic Maximizer has been around a long time, but it's been very popular for adding extra punch and clarity to a mix by "realigning" various frequency ranges to compensate for inherent monitor speaker driver delays (go check out the BBE website for a complete explanation at www.bbesound.com). Lots of hardware and software provide similar processing to make your mix sound fuller, punchier, brighter, louder, and lots of other 'ers.

Industry trends also dictate objectives when mastering a project. The most notable change over the past several years is the "necessity" to make final masters as loud as possible—no matter what the content is. By applying limiters with low-level adjustments, we can virtually eliminate all dynamic range from a sound file so it sounds consistently loud. Many engineers and artists decry this practice as it destroys the musicality of the song, but record companies these days will often reject masters that don't "sound as loud as the competition". Here's a before and after example of a mix that was processed with a plug-in limiter, set to bring up the low-level dynamics as well. Note how the waveform loses much of the ups and downs, looking more consistent from left to right and remaining close to the top and bottom edges of the window (close to these edges means higher signal level). These ups and downs represent level changes, which generally translate into perceived volume differences. So, the processed example will not vary much in apparent volume, but rather will sound loud all the way through the song.

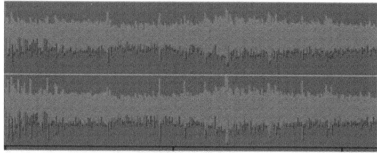

Unprocessed mix

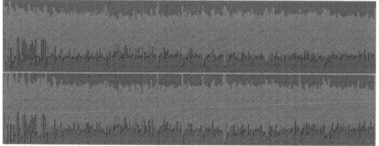

Compressed mix using mastering limiting plug-in (Peak)

Audio examples 84, 85, & 86: Raw mix, mastered mix using Peak software, mastered mix with BBE Sonic Maximizer (Lo=3.3, Process=3).

Audio example 87: Another mix using BBE Sonic Maximizer (out/in).

Here's an interesting example of a Grammy-winning, platinum-selling album that needed a little more attention during mixing and mastering. The following plot compares one song from this record with another much better sounding recording. You'll notice that the low-frequencies have a huge boost with a corresponding severe drop-off in the high frequencies. So what does this record sound like? Just like it looks on the chart: boomy on the bottom and dull on the high end. It was a good musical album, but hardly a stellar example of engineering performance.

into the board twice at the same time—from the microphone inputs as well as from the multitrack outputs as they are being recorded. Tracks already recorded are coming into the board, possibly into the same IO modules as that being used by incoming mic signals. What madness! Let's cut through this muck.

It's important to understand what an input/output module does on a console. (Note that there are two main types of console designs: inline and split. These will be explained in Chapter 9: *Recording Consoles*, so for now we'll base our discussion on inline consoles, which are the most common these days.) Each channel input has up to three input connectors on the back: mic, line, and multitrack/tape. There are two separate signal paths running down each module, referred to as *channel* and *monitor*. Let's explain these first.

The *channel path*, also referred to as the *mic* or *recording path,* contains the incoming microphone or line-level signal. When you plug a mic in and run it through the board, you are using the channel path for this signal. The channel path signal flows through the IO module, is then routed to an output bus by the assignment matrix (those numbered buttons on each channel), where it is sent to the multitrack recorder. Simple so far.

That signal (along with others which are already recorded) comes back from the recorder into the multitrack returns of the console. The outputs of the multitrack are usually permanently wired to the corresponding channel number on the board, i.e. track one = channel one, etc. These MT return inputs use the *monitor path* of each IO module, rather than the channel paths. They come in and flow through each module, then are routed to the console's main mix bus, which in turn feeds the monitoring system in the control room (so you can hear everything) as well as the 2-track and CD recorders. Not so bad yet.

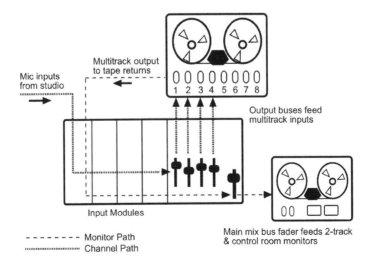

You can look at this as two separate mixers in one unit. The engineer must set mic levels as they are routed to the multitrack. This can be done without actually turning up the control room monitors. However, to hear everything, you've got to use the "second" mixer—the monitor paths that get their signals from the multitrack outputs, via the MT returns on each IO module. Both channel and monitor paths have their own level controls.

Now, if you route each incoming microphone to the same numbered track as the channel it's plugged into, things are fairly straightforward. For example, if you've got a kick drum mic coming in mic input 1, you can route it to track 1 on MT. Here you are controlling the recording level as well as the monitor return on the same channel, but using the different physical controls on that module associated with each signal path.

It gets more challenging when you route incoming mics to a different numbered track on the MT. Why would you do this? Say you just recorded a lead vocal on track 17, and the mic is plugged into mic channel 17 on the board. Now you want to record another vocal track, a harmony part. You need to record this to a different track, say 18, but you don't want or need to reconnect the mic into another channel. You've already got all the levels and EQ set for this particular vocalist—no need to reset all this. Just re-assign this channel to a different track on MT, 18, using the assignment matrix. Now, track 17 will still be heard through the console monitor path on channel 17. The new part will still be coming in the board on channel path of module 17, but you will use the monitor path on module 18 to hear it.

Thus two different signals are simultaneously running through module 17. The first vocal track is coming in on monitor 17, the new part coming in channel 17 being routed to track 18 on MT, then returning into monitor 18 on the console. Make sense? It will once you start actually trying it yourself, though it takes awhile to become really comfortable, especially during a hectic session. Here is the summary of where a microphone signal goes during a recording take:

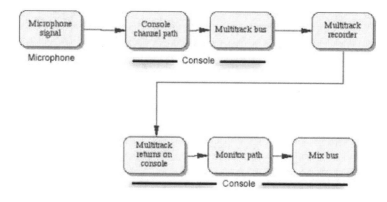

The overall issue to remember is to keep **channel** and **monitor** paths clear and distinct in your mind. They are separate signals, even if they happen to be flowing through the same numbered channel module on the console. Certain functions are always done to the channel path signal, others to the monitor path, and sometimes it depends on the situation. So, the mic signal always flows through the channel path on its way to an output bus that sends it to the multitrack recorder. These signals always return through monitor paths on the console that feed the mix bus (and therefore your control room speakers). Now, do you want to EQ a mic signal so it gets recorded that way? Set the EQ into the channel path where the mic is plugged in. Do you want to record a snare drum with compression? Insert the compressor into the channel path of the mic signal. Cue mixes are almost always sent from the monitor paths (multitrack returns), so turn up your cue aux sends from the modules corresponding to the tracks on multitrack (not the mic channels)—then make sure you source these to monitor path. It'll take awhile for you to get a clear operating picture of this, but focus on these principles while you practice and you'll get it.

For now let's back up and step through the process of getting ready to hit that record button.

Getting the Equipment Ready

Control room setup

You need to arrive much earlier than the clients so you can get the equipment cleaned and set up for the session. Here's what you need to do:

The Room

Turn on all equipment as soon as you arrive. As electronic equipment warms up the calibration and operation of the internal parts adjust. What this means is that the gear will sound different after it's been on awhile. Many studios leave their main devices such as consoles and tape machines on *all* the time.

Check to make sure everything is working. It's a serious bummer when the session actually begins and you then discover the tape machine has flipped a logic board or something. There will be plenty to worry with when everyone arrives—do what you can to reduce session delays and tense emotions.

Clean the room up. Get the trash out from last night's session, pick up extra cables and gear, and straighten anything lying around. Make your studio look professional to your clients—most of them will notice.

The other thing you'll have to deal with as the session begins is all the people who will show up. Some of these are necessary, such as the producer, chief engineer, and other assistant engineers. Hired musicians will show up as they are needed during the course of recording the various tracks, since they are often paid by the hour or "call" block (union terms). If a band has booked the studio for a project then usually the entire band will hang around. Unfortunately, family members and friends will often show up because they're "with the band". They just get in the way, make noise, and generally become a nuisance factor just to annoy you. You'll have to be ready for this in your control room layout and space, possibly establishing rules ahead of time for who's allowed in which rooms during the sessions. You definitely need to control access to rooms that contain equipment so you don't begin losing inventory while you're busy getting sounds just right.

- Turn up the monitor fader on each multitrack return channel (monitor path).

To set final recording level to multitrack

- Unmute each mic input channel (mute switch off).
- Turn up mic pre trim while the musician is playing or singing.

One last thing on the console

Now that you've got levels to the recorder and can hear them in the control room monitors, a separate mix of these tracks needs to be sent to the headphones in the studio. This is called the cue mix, and this is what allows the musicians to hear what is already on multitrack as well as the new parts they are currently recording.

You will use an aux send from each channel to send out to the studio headphone system. If you recall, we used auxiliary sends during mixdown to send copies of certain tracks to the outboard processing gear, such as for reverb. Aux sends don't necessarily mean reverb—they are merely additional outputs that take a copy of that channel's signal and send it wherever you want.

Aux sends work well for cue mixes because you basically create an entirely separate mixer. For example, many studios will permanently connect aux 1 & 2 from the console to their headphone amplifier. Since there is an aux 1 & 2 on each channel, you can send any (or all) of your tracks to either (or both) of these outputs. Why two auxes? You can set up your studio to have two entirely separate cue mixes, or you can have one stereo mix, aux 1 feeding the left side of the headphones and aux 2 feeding the right side. Many recording consoles conveniently provide stereo aux sends, so you can use one send and pan accordingly—much easier.

One last important step—make sure you push the little button called *pre* beside the aux send control on each channel. Simply put, an aux send takes a copy of the signal flowing through a channel and sends it wherever you want. Now, the issue is where exactly in the channel does it come from. A normal aux send setting comes after the main channel fader, so any changes on this fader level will also affect how much goes out the aux send. During a tracking session, however, the musicians need their own mix of the tracks, and they don't want this mix to change while the engineer and producer move faders around (which is inevitable). So, we need to *source* the aux signals *before* the channel faders, which is what the *pre-fader* button does. Bottom line—every time you are tracking with a cue mix, automatically select all cue aux sends as pre-fader.

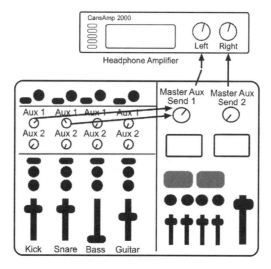

The master aux outputs are then connected to a headphone amplifier, which in turn feeds the headphones in the studio. (All speakers, including headphones, require amplified signals to work.) Some mixers provide a built-in headphone amplifier.

Once you become proficient at setting up the console for a tracking session you should get into the habit of establishing the cue mix as soon as possible. The musicians are already in the studio attempting to make noise into the mics and hear themselves—it's very frustrating for them if it takes forever to hear anything in the cans (headphones). It's better to go ahead and turn up the auxes you will use on all channels and get the cue ready for signal—then when you turn up each mic level the cue mix will already be set.

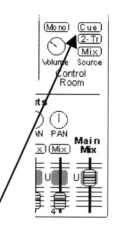

One last word of advice here. All consoles have the feature of selecting the aux outputs in the control room monitors. Remember how you selected the main mix as your listening source? You can also select the master aux outputs to hear their respective mix of the signals. (It may be labeled differently, such as *cue* on this diagram.) Listen to this periodically so you can hear the same blend that the musicians are getting. It's never the same as that in your control room mix, so sympathize with them and make sure you understand what they're getting in the

As the band is playing, don't just sit back and kick your feet up on the board. On the track sheet, notate which tracks are being recorded and particularly note the time locations for cue points in the song, i.e. first verse, first chorus, second verse, second chorus, bridge, etc. With these you can quickly find any section of the song to fix a part or add a new track.

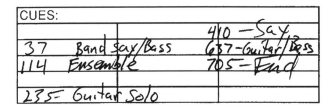

Fixing and Overdubbing

Once the first pass is complete, immediately go back to the beginning of the recording or to a section that needs to be fixed due to a mistake during the performance. Professional musicians will immediately tell you where they need to fix a note or phrase—if you are a musician you should already have heard and noted these problems. Don't just dumbly wait to be told what needs to be done. Try to anticipate what the producer and musicians will need to work on. Have copies of the music charts or scores so you can follow along—it will speed up the session and help you work more closely with the others.

Take the tracks out of record ready except for the part that you need to fix. To fix a bad spot, referred to as *punching in*, rewind before the problem location, play the MT and have the musician play along. When you get to the spot, find an opening in the performance and quickly hit the record button. The recorder will continue playing, but will now be recording the new performance on that track. When you pass the problem area, find an opening and hit the play button to take the track out of record mode. Go back and listen to make sure the punch is smooth. You may need to take a minute before recording to find a decent place to punch in and out—it can be difficult to get it right, but it gets easier with practice and experience.

Once the basic tracks have been fixed, you can either go on and record basics for the next song or begin overdubbing on the first tune. If you are changing mic setups for the next recording, make sure you bring down all mic trims (preamps) and mute the channels. Anytime you move or plug/unplug a mic you send a serious jolt through the system which can damage something.

Remember how we described the console monitor mix setup? Since all your monitoring has been established from the multitrack returns, and not the mic inputs, the basic tracks you've just completed will still be heard through those monitor channels—even though the microphones are no longer connected. To overdub a new track, simply route the new mic input to an unused track and turn up the monitor levels on that console channel (don't forget the cue aux sends).

Confused yet?

It takes awhile to get used to all the details involved in tracking—that's why we started with mixing. Just keep it simple as you practice and follow these steps carefully so you gradually get the hang of it. Once you feel comfortable with the buttons, faders, and numbers, spend more of your energies listening to the sounds you are getting from the mics and equipment. The main priority for getting high quality sounds is placing an instrument in a good room, putting the right mic in the right place, and having a great musician play. However, you cannot concentrate on this if you're still figuring out which buttons to push and which to avoid. The next section might best be read after you've gotten the hang of it and are ready to get down to business—we're going to explain some of the miking and recording issues you'll run into and how to handle them.

Getting Great Sounds From Your Mics

Just as we did in the mixdown chapter, we're going to point out several situations that occur during tracking and provide some possible solutions. Learn to use your ear and experiment; once you're comfortable with the equipment and procedures you can pay more attention to the more important task of getting good sounds. Some of these will sound very similar as in the mix chapter—they are, and this is the time to make sure these problems don't get recorded to begin with, requiring you to fix them during mixing.

It doesn't sound like a snare drum to me

Explanation:

Many times you'll place a microphone on an instrument, turn it up in the control room, and wonder what happened. You look to make sure that it is indeed a snare drum you're working with, but it doesn't sound right.

Solution:

Don't reach for the EQ. Go into the room and listen to the drum itself. Get a feel for what it's supposed to sound like so you know what you are shooting for. Here are a few things to try:

- *Move the mic around.* Even a few inches either direction can make a big difference, especially in terms of how close the mic is. Acoustic instruments need space and time for their sound to develop, so if you put a mic an inch away from a drum head you're never going to get the fullness of what the drum actually sounds like. Pull it back several inches and see if that helps.

- *Use a different mic.* All mics are not created equal, and that's intentional. Each mic has its own characteristic sound and particular way it picks up different sound sources, so experiment. Over time you'll build your own repertoire of what mics you like for certain instruments and voices.

- *Work on the instrument itself.* A good musician knows how to fine-tune their instrument for the best possible sound. Some have no clue, so the more you know about different instruments the more you can come to the rescue.

- *Move the instrument in the room.* Many rooms have different sonic characteristics throughout the space—try another location and see what happens.

The main issue here is to avoid the common reaction of using EQ to fix bad mic choice and placement. Your goal should be getting as clean and perfect a sound as possible into the mic itself—then if needed use some EQ or other processing to help out.

I can't get enough level on the mic

Explanation:

Once you set the console and recorder and begin turning up the mic trim, you may not get enough signal on the meters, even if you go all the way with the mic pre. There are a couple of reasons this can happen.

- The musician is not playing or singing at full volume. Often a musician will only talk into the mic, or lightly play their instrument since they're not in the full swing of the tune. This is a much lower sound level than you'll get during the recording, so try to have them play normal—ask them to rehearse their parts or something.

- Dynamic mics have a lower signal output than condenser mics. The microphone chapter will explain these terms, but for now just remember that some mics aren't as "loud" as others. If you put an AKG 414 on an acoustic guitar, then replace it with a Shure SM57, you'll have to crank up the 57 higher to get anything through the console. (The reverse is also important: if you have a dynamic mic on a source, then replace it with a condenser without changing levels, you'll likely get a nasty surprise as your speaker cone shoots across the room...or something like that.)

- The mic may just need to be closer to the sound source. Many instruments such as classical guitars, guitars with nylon strings, and some singers don't put out a lot of sound, so you need to move the mic closer. It's better to get closer than having to crank all your gain controls wide open.

If you still cannot get enough level to the multitrack, and you're certain it's not your equipment (you've successfully gotten other mics to work), then you can use the output bus fader as another level control. We said earlier that the output buses should be set at unity and left alone, but if you need extra amplification that the mic pre cannot provide, then go ahead and turn these faders up. Some consoles actually have two different level controls in addition to the mic pre, so balance these to help (don't turn one way up and leave the other way down). Also, some multitrack recorders feature their own input level controls.

It sounds muddy and boomy

There are a couple reasons that your sounds are muddy or boomy on the low end.

Explanation #1:

With certain types of microphones, close placement to the sound source results in a low-frequency boost called *proximity effect*. This occurs with directional mics such as cardioid (uni-directional), hyper-cardioid, super-cardioid, and bi-directional. Omni-directional mics are not affected by this.

Example:

The acoustic guitar sounds unnaturally boomy when close-miked to the instrument.

Check your console I/O module setup

- Bus assignment selected?
- Output bus level turned up?
- Mic/Line input selected?
- Phantom power on (for condenser mics)?
- Mic preamp turned up?

If you're using a dynamic mic, remember that your source may not be playing/singing very loudly for a sound check. You may just need more gain— but be careful that everything is set correctly first.

Check mic and connections in the studio.

- Turn down mic pre & mute channel first.
- Check switches on the mic (pads, polar patterns).
- Make sure mic cable is plugged securely into the mic.
- Verify mic cable is plugged securely into correct mic input.

Still no signal? Go through each of these *one at a time*.

- Replace the mic cable – then verify.
- Try a different mic input (remember to change on the console too).
- Try a different mic.

Most of the time it's user error, something simple like not fully plugging a microphone cable in, plugging into the wrong mic patchbay input, missing something on the console I/O module, etc. If you do find a broken cable or microphone, label and set it aside so you can fix it later. If the mic itself is not passing signal after you've tried at least two different cables and verified the console setup, you can look for something on the mic. Make sure the XLR pins are tight in the casing. Sometimes this connector pulls loose, possibly pulling the wires inside. The other common problem results from the mic capsule getting struck by a drumstick or overeager vocalist. Contact your studio manager or service technician.

Chapter Eight

Engineering Records in the Studio: Pre-production, Politics, & Paperwork

Before you set foot in the studio a lot of information needs to be hashed out. You and your client must meet to discuss various aspects of the project, including the purpose of the project, goals they have in mind, and how they want to achieve them. All parties involved must be totally clear (it rarely happens) as to what they each expect from this project. Why? If you deliver a product they disagree with, it may mean whether or not you get paid (or sued) for all your work—I'd say that's a pretty important issue.

Session Planning (Client's Perspective)

Purpose

Why are you doing this? Is this to promote your song(s), or your group, or both? Will this be a demo, and for what audience, or is it a full-blown album for distribution and sale?

Goals

What exactly do you want at the end? One song or ten songs? Radio play or just copies to sell at gigs? This determines the methodology, quantity of songs, and final product (CD, downloads, MP3s).

Methodology

How are you going to get there? Multitrack vs 2-track? What type of studio? Will you be hiring musicians, arranger, and a producer? Have you rehearsed to perfection? Determine what musical parts are needed and which are optional. Work out your arrangements before the session. Make music in the studio, not major musical decisions. Has the rhythm section practiced by themselves if you're overdubbing everything else? Organize similar tunes and parts to minimize studio setup and changeover time. *Remember your budget.* Oh yeah, how much money do you have? I've seen poor planning result in lots of over-budget projects, and therefore very irate clients and record companies.

Session Planning (Engineer's Perspective)

Get familiar with the project. What type of music is it? Instrumentation? Are you familiar with that particular style of music? Can your studio handle the project? One of the few non-label projects I worked on involved a band who visited the studio to see what kind of setup we had. They brought several CDs, listened through the control room monitors, and asked lots of questions—all to determine whether our facility and staff were appropriate for what they wanted to do. I was impressed, and we had a great time working with them.

Goals

Make completely sure you and the client are in total agreement with what the final outcome should be. Let me repeat that—make absolutely sure you all understand what you're trying to accomplish as this is a major cause for conflict and budget over-runs.

Methodology

Plan how to best accommodate their goals. This includes studio setup, mic choice, tracking schedule, equipment needed, supplies needed, mastering needs. Do this well before the dates for the sessions, lest you be caught unawares. Having no 2-inch tape or spare hard drives is quite embarrassing when Dave Matthews shows up ready to play…

Depending upon the studio, some of this pre-production planning and communication will fall upon the studio manager and/or producer. If so, then a work order will be filled out with the necessary information for the engineer and seconds (assistants) to prepare for the sessions.

Who's in Charge? Session Politics & Roles

Producer

The bane of any recording session is when everybody claims equal input, such as the members of a band. It is *imperative* that the client (or record label) hire a qualified producer who has done this before. This individual must know the particular style of music and should have worked with the group to know "their sound". The producer has overall authority for the project and is responsible for:

- Overall production concept
- Business management
- Musical direction
- Artistic decisions

We once did a rare non-label album project that featured a band with seven members—and each one had different opinions. This is normal, but there was no one person designated to make final decisions, so everybody tried to influence the outcome. We spent an inordinate amount of time replacing basic tracks and solos, often when existing tracks were more than good enough. I spent an entire night (read that as about twelve hours) overdubbing a guitar part throughout one song. There must be at least eighty-seven punches in that five minute track, simply because the player kept changing his mind as we went along. A producer would have stopped this long before dawn, realizing that what we had early on was sufficient, especially considering that the musician was a fabulous player—no need to redo anything. The producer is ultimately responsible to the record company who is fronting the money for the album. The task is to complete projects satisfactorily, on time, and under budget. After all, it's the artist's money that's ultimately being spent…but that's a different book.

Many prospective students tell me they wish to become record producers upon graduation. However, there is no official certification to be a producer. These individuals learn their craft over time, many while serving as engineers on other projects, then branching out to do a few projects on their own. Gifted producers seem to know just what to do to get the most from their artists and musicians. I was privileged to work on a large number of albums with a man who had that magic touch. Everybody wanted to work with him, and it was easy to see why. Once we had a vocal trio who had just hired a new vocalist. She was nervous and could not quite make it through one particular part of a song. They kept up the pressure and she simply broke down. I got ready to turn everything off and go home, but this producer told me to mute the mic and give them ten minutes. I have no idea what he said to her (I was too honest to listen in), but when he came back we ran tape and she nailed it perfectly in one take.

If you are interested in producing, spend time listening closely to how producers put together the records you enjoy. Even better, listen to lots of different styles—it's rare you get to work in only one particular genre. Producers get paid by the job and find work with bands and companies who like their style and see a successful track record. Good producers not only get paid a flat fee for the project, but can also negotiate points, or a percentage, of the royalty income from album sales.

Chief Engineer

This is the primary engineer responsible for listening to the producer and getting their ideas on the recording. Your job is to always be ahead of the producer. You must listen to the music, know where the sections are (verse, chorus, bridge), listen for wrong notes, chords, and intonation problems. Read the producer's mind and know what they'll be doing next. Depending upon the situation you might offer creative, musical input. In smaller projects and studios you might be functioning as both—which absolutely demands musical skills and a good ear...hint, hint.

Chief engineers are sometimes employed by the studio, but often major projects are handled by independent engineers who are hired per job. They therefore work in lots of different facilities, which requires getting used to the nuances between different sounding rooms with different equipment. Spend some time reading album credits and note the names that keep appearing on various projects.

Assistant Engineer

These are the silent runners that keep everything moving. They handle studio setup before the session, tear-down afterwards, keeping notes and track sheets during the session, manning the recorders, adjusting mic stands, making coffee, making pizza runs... Your job is to always be ahead of the producer and engineer and not get in the way. The hours are long, the demands are high, and it takes a lot of initiative and positive attitude to impress anybody (i.e. keep your job and move up the food chain).

Being an assistant means different things depending on the type of facility. Smaller companies may provide more opportunity for new engineers to get their feet wet early and do some engineering. Larger, high-end studios may make newcomers wait months before they touch a console, taking the time to observe the recruit and see how determined and motivated they are. If you are willing to stay in for the long haul there are opportunities, but it can be a long, grueling process. In the meantime, keep your mouth shut, ask questions when appropriate, and learn from the more experienced engineers and producers. We've had a few interns over time who didn't understand this concept—they arrogantly thought they should offer their opinions and have never worked in the big leagues since.

Always remember you're there to make music. It is critical that the artists feel absolutely comfortable when they play. Any uncertainty, frustration, or lack of emotion will be obvious on the record. The mark of a top-notch producer/engineer is knowing how to pull the best out of people no matter what their abilities are. 80% of the music industry is communication skills. Knowing how to translate non-musical, non-engineering terms into your lexicon and vice-versa goes a long way to keeping everybody happy and on track. It's pretty simple really—be nice to the good folks and stop trying to prove something.

Session Paperwork

Any professional business is run on paperwork. Sometimes it tends to get out of hand, but you've got to get into the habit of organizing your studio and the projects you work on. Students always ask "But why? It's so annoying and time consuming." It's simple—if you don't track your expenses and time in the studio, how can you bill the client? If you don't keep careful inventory of project media, how do you know which reel or drive is okay to record over? What happens after you've been in business for ten years and have hundreds of files to sift through when the long-time client wants to remix that classic hit from the nineties?

You get the idea. Let's show you a few sample documents that you'll use everyday.

- Work orders
- Invoices
- Instrument setup / mic input list
- Track sheets
- Take sheets
- Media labeling
- Tape logs
- Time logs
- Maintenance reports

Work order

Client: Engineer: Project #:
Contact phone:
Contact address:

Pre-production	Date Completed	Initials
❏ Session booked		
❏ Producer booked		
❏ Musicians booked		
❏ Budget agreed		
❏ Deposit received $_____		

Recording	Date Completed	Initials
❏ Microphone rentals needed:		
❏ Equipment rentals needed:		
❏ Tracks complete		
❏ Rough mix to producer		
❏ Rough mix to artist		
❏ Mix complete		
❏ Master quality assurance		
❏ Final invoice to label		
❏ Balance of invoice paid		
❏ Master delivered to label		

	Date
Signatures	
Label representative:	
Studio representative:	

Hear Real Good Studios
101 N Audible Ave
Deafness, ZM, 90909
909-555-9090

This is a simple work order used for album projects that allows all individuals involved to ensure everything is planned for and completed.

Mic Input Chart

Engineers need to keep detailed, accurate notes as they set up for sessions. Write down everything you plug in, including mic inputs, outboard gear patches, etc. A mic input sheet is a simple chart indicating which microphone is plugged into which mic input on the patch panel in the studio. This usually correlates to the same numbered channel input on the console, but does not indicate track numbers on multitrack.

List your mic inputs, which mics are connected, and what instruments or locations they're being used for. Make sure you update this as the session progresses, such as for overdubs or anytime you change mics.

Mic input	Microphone	Location
1	Shure Beta 52	Kick Drum
2	Shure SM57	Snare
3	Neumann KM84	High Hat
4	Sennheiser 421	Hi Tom
5	Sennheiser 421	Mid Tom
6	Sennheiser 421	Lo Tom
7	Shure SM81	Left Overhead
8	Shure SM81	Right Overhead

So, why is this so helpful? Once the session begins things can get hectic very quickly. At some point you will have a mic signal disappear or experience some unexpected change in your signal flow. With everybody staring at you waiting for you to fix it, it's your job to know exactly what's going on. Accurate notes will enable you to go directly to the problem to see what's wrong.

Often these charts are provided by the chief session engineer ahead of time so the assistant can have everything ready to go before everyone else shows up.

This track sheet records everything you need to know about each song: which instruments are on which tracks, cue points in the song, general notes from the engineer or producer, project title and studio info, and technical information about the recording itself. This sheet remains with the multitrack masters where anybody can later easily find what's on the tape or drive.

Music Technology　　　　　　　　　　　　　　**Take Sheet**
Lebanon Valley College
Annville, PA 17003

Work Order # ___*0010033*___　　Producer ___*Frederick*___

Album/Project ___*LA Jean*___　　Engineer ___*H.Y*___

Reel/Tape # ___*00343*___　　Studio ___*A*___

　　　　　　　　　　　　　　　　Date ___*5/18/89*___

Take #	Time	Code	Remarks
1	:21	CT	OK –
2	4:13	FS	—
3	4:14	FS	–
4	4:19	IC	
5	5:42	CT	Keeper – Destroy use V2 from T1

Codes: CT = Complete Take   IC = Incomplete Take   FS = False Start

This take sheet is used during the basic tracking of a song. Each time the musicians begin a song, a notation is made as to what counter time each take was begun, whether or not they completed the take, and whether it was a keeper.

128

```
Client:                    Project #:
Engineer:                  Date:

Tape speed:  ☐ 30 ips   ☐ 15 ips   ☐ 7 1/2 ips

Tracks:      ☐ Mono    ☐ Stereo   ☐ 4 tr

Wound:       ☐ Tails out  ☐ Heads out      NR ☐
_____

Track list                         Time start




                 Hear Real Good Studios
                   101 N Audible Ave
                  Deafness, ZM 90909
                    909-555-9090
```

An analog tape label

So, what have we accomplished so far?

At this point you should understand basically how recording sessions work. We've discussed the equipment, the facilities, and the people involved, including various career options in the field. Each step in the production process has been explained, and if you have been using the audio CDs you've begun to hear some of the issues and concepts we've talked about.

Hopefully this part of the book has provided a clear overview of studio recording and helped get your feet wet. The remainder of the book is designed to provide a condensed, clear explanation of the theory and operation behind what we've just covered. It's enough to get you going, but you need to purchase one of the many excellent books available that cover theoretical concepts in greater detail. Since there's already so much out there it's pointless to duplicate it all here.

Be sure to re-read the first few chapters and practice on your own gear. These fundamentals will provide the foundation for developing your engineering skills, something many self-taught recording types lack (and it shows in their work). Happy recording—make some good music and remember to send me my 10% cut of anything you make.

**This is the end of side two.
Turn the tape over now to listen to side three.**

During mixdown, you would assign each input channel to the main stereo mix bus, which sends it to your master 2-track recorder. This might be labeled 2-mix, L-R mix, etc. Note that some boards don't require this, the multitrack returns being automatically routed to the mix bus.

Pan Potentiometer

Use the pan control, or *pan pot,* to place that particular track somewhere in the left-right stereo image. This allows you to position a guitar off to the left while putting a backup vocalist off to the right.

You can find the pan by looking for a single pot near the fader labeled either *pan* or *left-right.* Pretty difficult, huh?

Channel Mute

The last main feature we'll point out here is the mute button. This turns off that channel. This is useful for turning off a vocal track before they begin singing (so their coughing or complaining doesn't get recorded in the mix).

The mute button is usually found near the fader and pan, and is usually labeled *mute.* Equally difficult stuff.

Output and Monitoring

Output Buses

Output buses connect signals coming through the input channels to particular tracks on the multitrack recorder or stereo mix recorder. Some consoles provide a separate set of faders for these busses. During tracking, when you assign a mic signal to a certain numbered output, this is the fader that receives that signal and sends it on to the recorder.

Tip: During a mixdown you can try using them as sub-mixers. For example, you could assign all your drum tracks (kick, snare, high hat, toms, overheads) to one stereo pair of sub-buses. Then, if you need to lower the volume of the drums during the mix, you simply pull these two faders down, rather than grabbing all eight or so drum channel faders.

Stereo Main Mix Bus

The stereo main mix bus directly feeds the 2-track recorder, which can be an analog, CDR, or flash recorder.

Keep this fader at the unity point, which is indicated by either a "U" or "0". Once set, forget about it during the mix and adjust all levels with individual channel faders.

Control Room Monitor Level

The stereo mix bus also directly feeds your control room monitor speakers. There's a separate volume control for this, usually located on the right side or center of the console.

It's important to understand the difference between the mix bus fader and the control room volume pot. The mix fader controls the mix level going to the 2-track recorders. You don't want to change this during the recording.

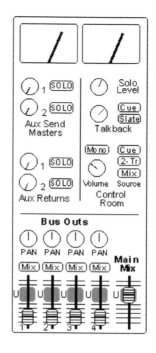

Since you're undoubtedly going to turn the volume up and down while you work (such as when the pizza guy shows up), you use the separate volume control which only affects what you're hearing—not the mix levels being recorded.

VU Meters

All consoles provide at least a pair of visual signal strength indicators, called VUs. These may be the moving needle type or a series of LEDs that light up as the signal gets stronger.

These are vital in making sure you're not recording anything too low or too hot, thereby risking excess noise and/or distortion. Always keep your eyes on these meters to make sure you're running good levels.

Master Aux Outputs

As mentioned in the input channel overview, the aux sends on all channels combine together at the master aux send level controls. There is one per aux send, meaning that if your board has six auxes, there will be six master aux level pots on the right side of the console.

Remember the term "unity" mentioned earlier? Same thing here. Try to keep your aux masters as close to this point as possible, using the individual channel controls to balance the overall signals. How do you find "unity"? Rotary pots usually have unity at the 12:00 position (straight up), though some label unity at the fully-clockwise position. It may be labeled unity, U, or zero.

Aux sends *send* your sounds to effects devices such as reverb, which are located external to the console (therefore the term *outboard gear*).

Aux Returns

However, to hear the reverb'd sound, you've got to bring it back into the console and add it to the overall mix. It doesn't just magically add it within the console.

So, you take the output from your effects boxes and plug them into the aux returns of the board. On the right side of the console, you have control over the incoming level of the effect, panning, and maybe some EQ as well. You need one mono aux return per effects device you're using, two each if you're running stereo from the box.

A few other technical items to know about

Patchbays

Many consoles have integrated patchbays. These are the long rows of connectors that are wired to all the inputs and outputs of your gear in the studio. So, instead of crawling behind everything to connect a compressor to channel 4, you only have to patch a short cable between the two jacks on the patchbay. If your console doesn't have one, you can easily set one up by purchasing the bays, which can be racked in a standard equipment rack, and then connecting everything in the back. If you're making your own, there are certain conventions to where things are located. First you need to understand the concept of how jacks relate to each other.

Normalled connections feature two jacks, usually adjacent to each other, which are connected in the back so that the signal coming from one jack will flow into the second without having to patch a cable between them. The reason for this is to facilitate making connections that are used all the time, thereby reducing the amount of patching that must be done. For example, since the multitrack output buses on a console nearly always feed the same numbered tracks on the recorder, studios will *normal* the bus outputs to their related MT inputs. You still have the two jacks on the patchbay in case you need to re-direct somewhere else. Another example is to automatically have certain aux sends feed specific effects devices. If aux 4 is normalled to your Reverberator XL, then all you have to do is turn up aux 4 to get signal to the unit without having to patch the cable. By patching a cable into either of the two jacks you will break the internal connection, allowing you to redirect the signal.

Half-normalled connections are similar to normalled jacks, except that if you patch into one of the jacks the signal will still flow to the other jack. It takes patching cables into both jacks to break the normalled connection. Insert points, discussed earlier when we were connecting compressors and noise gates, are always wired half-normalled. Why do this? A couple of reasons, one being that you can use the insert send jack alone to send a copy of that channel's signal somewhere while retaining the original signal flow. The internal connection remains unbroken, and yet you now have a copy of that signal to do something different with. Another nice use of this system is when you're setting up to record a bass guitar and want to add a compressor. You start by patching the first cable from the insert send to the input of the compressor. During the time it takes to then connect the second cable from the compressor output to the insert return, the original bass signal is still flowing through the channel without interruption. So what? So this means your bass player can keep playing without their cue feed being cut off while you reach for that second cable. This will make more sense when you actually try it...just trust me for now.

Open patchbay connections feature adjacent jacks that are not internally connected together—they're just individual jacks. An example of this might be the Line In jacks for each channel. They may not be wired to anything, and yet when you want to patch a CD player or effects output into an input channel, this is where you'd connect it.

Now that you sort of understand this, we can briefly outline typical layouts of patchbays. First, you want to line up outputs of gear that normally feed certain inputs all the time. Examples of this include multitrack bus outputs, which should be automatically connected to the inputs of your multitrack recorders. Same goes for the MT outputs, which always return to the same numbered channels on the console. So, MT Bus Out jacks (from the console) will fill one row of your patchbay while the MT Input jacks (to the recorder) will be located on the row directly above or below. You can do the same with aux sends, where

The final option is to forget the console entirely. Run ProTools or some similar system on your computer, buy a hardware control surface that looks like a console but is merely a physical controller for your software, and spend your money on quality microphone preamps.

Lastly, keep in mind that recording consoles are different from live reinforcement mixers. Recording requires that second monitor path capability (remember the tracking chapter?), and live boards do not have this. You can set up a simple live mixer to do some recording, but it's much easier and more powerful with a recording console.

Chapter Ten

Understanding and Using the Equipment:
Microphone Design

Design types

All microphones are *transducers*, which simply means they are devices that transfer one form of energy into another. Other transducers in audio include tape recorders, speakers, and phono cartridges.

Although the sole purpose of a microphone is to capture an acoustic event and convert it to an electrical signal, there are many ways to achieve this. None is particularly any better than another, and variation in mic design is deliberate so as to provide each microphone with a distinct sound. The result is an artist's palette of mics that provide different nuances to your recordings, so you can match just the right mic to that special soprano in your life.

The two main design principles that all microphones are based on are:

- Dynamic
- Condenser

Other variations in how any particular mic will sound involve types of materials used, circuit design, etc.

> Audio example 100: Comparing different mics using a pair of Shure KSM32 vs AKG 414.

Dynamic microphones

This design uses the principle of electromagnetic induction. A coil of wire is suspended within a magnetic field. The microphone diaphragm is attached to the coil, and when sound waves hit the diaphragm, this moves the coil of wire back and forth within the magnetic field. This generates an output voltage varying with the input movements. Why, you ask? It's physics – weren't you awake in class? So, the output signal varies analogous to the changes in the original acoustic sound wave...yes, that's where we get the term *analog*. Amazing.

Equivalent Noise

This is another rather obscure specification that few think about very often. All electronics make a small amount of noise as electrons move around doing their thing. This self-noise is quite minor compared to other noise sources in the recording chain, but is important with digital recording equipment as the noise floor is much lower than with analog recording. Any professional-quality microphone is sufficient, so don't spend your time trying to measure this stuff.

Impedance

This little-understood term is important in the design and connection for audio equipment. For now we'll just leave it as the mic's ability to provide a certain signal strength as compared to the mixer's requirements for input signals. Another way of saying this is that the console input is expecting a certain signal strength, so the microphone output must be designed to match this for optimum transfer of signal. Remember when you go to a concert and they have restricted gates and entrances to control the crowd going in? Think about if they either closed these nearly shut or opened everything completely. People would pile up trying to get in or you'd get a stampede. You get the idea.

In more practical terms, all professional microphones are low impedance, so don't use high-Z mics, which usually have 1/4" connectors and act as radio antennas for any available broadcast that happens to be floating through the room. Low-Z mics are much better at preventing outside interference and extraneous noise (motors, fluorescent lights, radios). High-Z mics also suffer from high-frequency loss over distance.

Balanced Microphone Cables

Professional low-Z microphones use mic cables employing two signal-carrying wires in addition to a ground wire (shield). These signal wires are twisted around each other throughout the cable, and the shield is most often braided around the two wires. This provides maximum protection from outside noise interference, or RF (radio frequency).

How does it do this? Audio signals are AC current, meaning they alternate positive/negative between the two signal wires. Any outside interference comes into the cable as a common polarity DC signal. When it arrives at the end it's cancelled out because all balanced audio gear (all professional equipment) is designed to accept AC signals only. The shield in the cable drains extraneous noise; it's shunted to ground.

XLR connectors are used, and the three pins are numbered so as to match on each end of the cable. Pin 1 is always the shield (ground); pins 2 and 3 carry the alternating polarity audio signal.

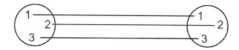

Each XLR connector has three pins for the three wires in a mic cable.

Phantom Power

Condenser microphones require an external power source, usually 48 volts DC. This is sent through the mic cable to the microphone, but does not damage the mic (or any other gear). Audio gear works with alternating current and looks for the *difference* between the two wires; phantom power is DC. Since there is no difference at the input it is ignored by the device.

PZM (Pressure Zone Microphone)

Ever notice those strange flat mics? These are called PZM mics, though the term PZM is actually a product trademark of Crown, Inc. The generic term is *boundary microphone*, and refers to a microphone where the mic element (diaphragm assembly) is mounted on a flat plate. The concept is to reduce phase cancellations that occur when miking a source using a traditional microphone

stand. With using a stand, the mic is elevated above floor level by several feet. The sound reaches the mic, but also bounces off the floor and into the mic, somewhat later than the original wave. Back to acoustics, but when two identical waveforms arrive at different times, phase cancellation occurs, which means the frequency response of the sound is altered in a negative way.

PZMs are popular for miking underneath a grand piano lid, on the floor, or on a wall. Try placing a close mic on a guitar cabinet, then adding a PZM on the floor or taped to the wall several feet away to capture the overall room sound.

Direct Box

These small boxes allow you to directly plug an electronic instrument into the mixer, such as a keyboard or guitar. They come in two types: passive and active. Active DIs require phantom or battery power, use active electronics, and provide a "hotter", typically higher quality signal output.

How to use a DI

- Plug output of instrument with 1/4" cable into DI box 1/4" input.
- Plug a mic cable from the XLR output of the DI into a mixer XLR mic input.

Features found on a DI

- 1/4" input (from instrument)
- 1/4" output (to an amplifier sitting close by if needed as a monitor)
- XLR output (to console mic input just like a microphone)
- Ground lift switch (eliminates ground loop hum—just switch it until the hum goes away or diminishes)
- Instrument/amp select switch—"amp" allows taking signal from the speaker out jack on a guitar amplifier. These are two very different signal levels, as the amp input expects a much higher signal level from the source.

DI boxes perform the following three functions:

- Reduces output level of instrument (line-level) to mic level.
- Changes the instrument's high-Ω output (unbalanced line) to a low-Ω source (balanced) needed for the mic input.
- Isolates audio signal, eliminating ground loop hum.

Features found on microphones

- Polar pattern select (some condensers allow you to change the directional pickup pattern)
- Attenuation pad to reduce incoming signal level (condensers)
- Low-cut filter to attenuate low frequency sounds (condensers & dynamics)
- Cable connector (XLR for professional microphones)

- Built-in ports for directional mics
- Not all mics offer all these controls.

Accessories

- Windscreen, also known as a pop filter. Hold your hand in front of your mouth and say stuff with lots of "p" and "b" sounds. Feel the puff of air? This will overload the mic diaphragm, causing those tremendous booms you heard in the school auditorium when your principal was lecturing to the student body. Another option is to place the mic slightly above the mouth, angled downward a bit. The air stream goes down, not up, so this can also take care of it.

- Shock mount. This microphone mount is designed to isolate the mic from vibrations that could be transmitted through the stand. They have an elastic strap which holds the mic so that it doesn't physically touch the plastic or metal of the mount.

- Stands and booms. The boom is the horizontal arm extender attached to the vertical stand. And you were worried about that one.

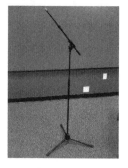

- Stereo stand adapter. This special item provides the means to mount two microphones on a single stand, most often in a specific stereo miking configuration.

Chapter Eleven

Understanding and Using the Equipment:
Basic Microphone Technique

So, now that you're impressed with all the various features and specifications of microphones, you're back to the basic question: How do I use these things and get a great sound? Microphone technique is very subjective; there are a few guidelines, but much is up to the individual, current trends, and the particular situation. The rule is not to worry about rules too much and just experiment. Sure, we'll give you a couple of things to keep in mind that might cause problems with your sounds, but generally you should just try lots of things to see what you like.

The first thing we'll tell you is to go listen to the instrument in the room before you pick up a microphone. What does it *really* sound like? Walk around, move your head, ask the musician where the sweet spots are as all instruments have different radiating characteristics (where the sound goes). Once you find a spot you like, now go pick a mic that best matches that sound. Not sure? No problem, just try a few. Too many young engineers throw a mic up and retreat to the control room and start turning EQ dials. Listen first, find the right mic, then find the right place for that mic. Always.

Placement options

In terms of where you put the microphone, the main variable is the distance from the source to the mic.

- Distant miking
- Close miking
- Accent miking
- Ambient miking

Distant Miking

For distant miking, the idea is to get a more rounded sound from your source blended with some room ambiance (reverb). The microphone could be anywhere from a few feet or all the way across the room.

Advantages

- Distant miking picks up more overall sound of the source, whether it is a single instrument or an entire ensemble. A sound source, especially more complex ones such as the piano or a choir, need space for the radiating sound to evolve and blend naturally, thus creating their characteristic sound we're accustomed to hearing.

- It also includes the surrounding acoustical environment which blends with the direct signal from the source. This balance is determined by the size of the source as well as size and characteristics of the hall or environment. Hear the difference between singing in a bathroom and singing in your living room?

However, if the room sounds bad, you need to try something different:

- Treat walls with absorptive material to reduce acoustical reverberation.
- Bring the mic closer to the source.

Boundary Interference

With distant miking it must be remembered that sounds radiating from the source not only travel directly to the mic, but also to surrounding surfaces such as walls, floor, ceiling, etc. These reflected waves will cause phase cancellation and attenuation at certain frequencies.

Solutions

- Install absorptive material on surfaces. You need to consider the difference in frequency ranges affected by types of acoustical treatments. Highs and lows are absorbed differently, so just laying carpet won't help you very much.
- Move the mic closer to the source—this will reduce the room effect on the sound.
- Use boundary mics on the floor or wall. These avoid phase issues (discussed later).

Close Miking

Place the microphone a couple of inches or even a few feet or so from the source, depending on the size of the source. For a guitar cabinet, you're talking 1-2 inches, whereas for a choir you're talking several feet.

Advantages

- Close, direct, tight sound.
- Excludes surrounding acoustical environment, including other instruments in the same room (to some extent).

When you place a mic close on a source all other sounds are much lower in level due to the inverse square law. Sounds complicated, but all this means is that as you double the distance between a sound source and the microphone, the level coming into the mic drops 4-6 dB. So, move any offending sounds farther away.

Placing a mic too close, though, results in a colored tonal quality – it doesn't sound natural. An example is the piano. Place a mic directly over one section of the strings within 6". You're not going to get the entire frequency range of the instrument, thus it won't have a normal piano sound.

Solutions

- Try moving the mic around a little.
- Move the mic away from the source.
- EQ some if you need to, especially to reduce any muddy regions caused by resonance (see the EQ chapter).

Leakage

Leakage is when a microphone picks up sound from a source other than its intended source. When multitracking you're usually aiming for tight control over individual parts or instruments. Leakage in a track colors not only that track, but especially its original track. This means that when you're mixing the song and work for that perfect snare track sound, you then turn on the kick track and wonder what happened to the snare. During the tracking session, snare sound leaked into the kick mic and will therefore affect how the snare sounds in the overall mix. Listen carefully to each of your tracks while you are tracking so you don't run into huge problems later. One example of an exception to this issue is recording a jazz combo. The nature of its traditional sound encourages some leakage associated with a live sound. However, severe coloration can ruin your day, so listen carefully and solo those tracks while you're getting mic levels.

Solutions

- Tighten miking distance.
- Use directional mics.
- Use gobos.
- Spread musicians out from each other (inverse square law).
- Use separate rooms (iso booths).
- Overdub later.

Phasing

Phasing is when two signals, identical or very similar, combine and destructively affect the sound. This can occur in a couple of ways:

- Electrically: One microphone cable is wired in reverse, meaning you have pin 2 connected to pin 3 on the other end of the cable.

- Acoustically: With two mics picking up the same sound source, any difference in path length between the source and each mic causes a timing discrepancy between the two signals, therefore inducing phase shift. Also, with one mic mounted above the floor, the reflected signal off the floor (or walls!) is delayed with respect to the direct signal. All frequencies are delayed the same amount, but since all frequencies have different wavelengths the phase shift varies up the scale. The result is a succession of dips and peaks in the frequency response (constructive and destructive interference). We call this the *comb-filter effect*. It sounds very colored in tonality.

Solutions

- Follow the **3:1 Rule**: For every one unit of distance between each mic and its source, the distance between mics needs to be at least 3 times that mic-to-source distance. So, make sure any other mics that are placed near a source are located farther away from the first mic.
- Use one mic (!)
- Use a boundary mic.

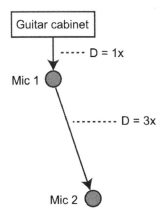

3:1 rule for using more than one mic on a source.

Audio examples 101 & 102: Close vs distant miking.

Audio examples 103 & 104: Kick drum mic close to beater, then farther back in drum.

Audio example 105: Adding individual drum mics on the set to hear how each part changes. Listen how the snare sounds different when toms/OH mics are on.

When miking vocals, be careful of side affects such as sibilance and explosive pops. Sibilance is excessive energy for the "s" sound, generally around 7 kHz or so. Pops come from hard consonants such as "p" and "b" where a great deal of wind is expelled downward from the mouth. Position the mic above the mouth pointing downward a tad and don't let the vocalist turn up into it. This helps for both of these conditions; if necessary you can position a pop-filter in front of the mic to reduce pops. During a mix you could also use a low-cut filter to some degree, though be careful not to lose part of the actual source sound.

Audio example 106: Sibilance.

Audio examples 107 & 108: Removing a vocal pop using a low-cut filter.

Accent Miking

When distant miking an ensemble occasionally certain parts get overshadowed. An example would be a soloist. Use a large-diaphragm directional mic and close-mic the instrument. Pan the signal true to the overall stereo image (as captured by the main stereo pair), and run it through a digital delay (set for a few ms - depending upon distances involved between accent mic and main stereo pair). This compensates for the difference in time of arrival to the accent mic and the stereo pair.

Ambient Miking

The concept here is to capture the sound of the room in order to add its natural acoustics to your recording. Mics are placed farther away from the source to get more of the environment than the direct sound. Usually stereo pairs of omnis or boundary mics mounted on the side or rear walls are used. You get natural reverberation and audience applause (if any).

Boundary Mics

As described earlier, the design of these mics make them ideal for reducing phase cancellations from direct vs reflected sound waves. They place the capsule right next to the reflecting surface (floor or wall) so the direct and reflected signals arrive simultaneously. Don't suspend a PZM in mid-air! You'll get a pronounced mid-range and attenuated low end. Tape them to the floor or walls using gaffer's tape. Boundaries are used a lot on grand pianos. Tape two of them to the bottom of the piano lid, one over the high strings, the other over the low end. You'll also find them on the front edge of stages during dramatic productions. They do very well picking up everything that happens on stage. Just be sure to put a piece of foam or rubber underneath to help reduce vibrations from movements on stage as your actors run around crazy-like. For ambient miking, tape them to the walls of the hall and make sure the stage manager is off-duty.

Helpful Tips You Won't Get Most Places

- Sound is different from the near field to the far field, meaning closer to the source versus farther back in the room. How is it different? Read on.

- The location in the room where the near field transitions into the far field is termed the *reverberation radius*. This is the boundary between the direct sound from your source and where the sound becomes more diffuse (reverberant). Any sound heard within the near field sounds dry

all the capsules already set up, or you can simulate the same arrangement using a cardioid and bi-directional mic.

So, how does it work? A signal coming in the front left would be picked up by the cardioid and the left (let's say this is the front side) of the Bi-D. These would add together and sound fine. However, a sound coming into the right (rear) of the Bi-D would tend to cancel when combined with the cardioid. (Bi-directional mics have a positive front and negative rear of the diaphragm.) Therefore the phase must be adjusted to allow both sides decent pickup. Manipulating this phase and level balance between the capsules allows adjustment of the stereo spread without having to physically move the mics. Very powerful.

You can purchase an M-S encoder/decoder, or you can simulate the same effect with gear you already have in the pantry. Take a cardioid mic and face it forward, then place a bi-directional mic against it facing left/right. Split the signal coming from the bi-d mic, using a mult on the patchbay, so you have two copies of this signal. Bring them into two different channels, bus to two different outputs, and invert phase on one channel. Pan them both center for now and bring both faders up until you get maximum cancellation—then mute. Bring the signal from the cardioid into a single channel on the console and bus it to the same two outputs as the Bi-D. Make sure levels are the same, unmute, pan the outputs. That's it.

Near-Coincident Systems

If coincident mics have capsules in the same physical space, near-coincident mics feature capsules that are not quite in the same space. The two mic capsules are placed a specified distance apart which allows time-of-arrival differences to help with stereo imaging. This method results in a better sense of spatial impressions. There are several variations of near-coincident configurations.

ORTF

This common type of near-coincident setup comes from the French National Broadcasting System (not that this bit of information was all that crucial...). Two cardioid mic capsules are placed 17 centimeters apart (about 6.7 inches) with an angle of 110°. This spacing corresponds to the distance between our ears (in case you don't have a ruler handy). Low frequency information comes largely from intensity differences, whereas high frequencies are determined through time-of-arrival cues since this range is highly directional.

NOS

This variation comes from the Dutch Broadcasting System. Two cardioid mics are spaced 30 centimeters and angled at 90°. Low frequency phase differences occur lower in the frequency bandwidth. This method has a more open sound than ORTF.

Jecklin Disk

This is an interesting derivation of the near-coincident technique where you mount a round disk *between* the two mics. The disk must be rigid and covered with an absorptive foam layer. The reason for all this fuss? This method provides a very pronounced stereo separation which is quite effective. The photo here is looking down from over top of the Jecklin Disk.

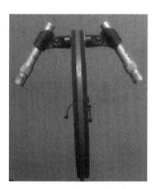

Spaced Pair Technique

Also known as **A-B**, this technique primarily follows the time of arrival principle, though intensity differences also contribute to localization. It is sometimes used in large rooms as the main stereo pair, and is also very popular for room (ambient) mics. Keep in mind, when placing mics at distances measured in feet you can introduce a hole in the middle. Left-side information will go mostly into the left mic, because due to the inverse-square law the signal will diminish enough not to be heard much in the right mic. You can place a third mic in the middle to grab the center information to fill in the hole. Large A-B is popular for large ensemble recording, often with a C mic in the middle. Small A-B arrangements can work quite well, such as off the end of a piano. Here are some guidelines to remember:

- There is no set distance between mics, though they should be less than 9' apart.
- If the sound source is very large, often a third mic (C) is added between A & B to fill in the middle.
- Use pressure omnis.

Disadvantages

- Potential comb-filter phasing due to distance between mics and to the sound source.
- Center image may not be very solid.
- Jet effect: For example, a violin begins playing on the far left side. The A (left) mic picks it up and we hear it in the left speaker. However, as the sound continues it reaches the B-mic (right), though with a time delay. This causes the sound to appear to be moving across the stereo field from left to right, which of course the actual violin is not doing.

Decca Tree

One of the most effective ways to capture an ensemble, especially a larger, deeper group such as an orchestra, is with a Decca Tree. This setup requires a special hardware stand that is essentially T-shaped, with a short base facing straight toward the back of the source and the longer top shaft facing sideways. A minimum of three mics are employed, one placed center and slightly forward of the two side mics. The center mic is pointed downward toward the rear of the group, and the two side mics face down toward either side, angled outward about 45 degrees or so. This provides better coverage of the depth of the group while maintaining accurate stereo localization. One variation is to add an additional mic on the extreme ends of the tree facing backwards towards the audience for surround recording.

Looking up at a Decca Tree configuration. The mic on the right is facing toward the back of the ensemble, while the other two capture the main left-right sections.

Support Mics

Often it may become necessary to pick up solo instruments or individual groups which may not be heard over the rest of the ensemble. A support mic is placed near the source, careful not to pick up other instruments around. Also of concern is the difference in time between it and the main stereo pair, and the difference in ambience. Sometimes a very slight delay may create the necessary first reflection occurrence to place it within the same ambience as the main mics.

Recording Acoustic Ensembles with Stereo Mic Techniques

So, what can you do with all this information? Whether you are laying horn and string tracks for a pop album or recording a large symphony, understanding single and stereo microphone techniques will help you capture the natural, acoustic sound you're after. Your goal in recording acoustic sources is to hear everything in their proper location on stage with a clear frequency response. Sometimes this requires littering the stage with microphones, many times it can be done with just two mics located in just the right spot. Learn the fundamental rules, such as 3:1 spacing, phasing issues, and room acoustics, then use your ears to determine what works and what doesn't for any given situation. First we'll provide some quick, basic acoustics issues to be aware of in any room or hall that help dictate where to place microphones. Then we'll discuss some general guidelines for recording large ensembles and smaller chamber groups.

Really Basic Room Acoustics Theory

The beginning of chapter fifteen (time-based processors) includes a short primer on room acoustics, but since I know you won't go to the trouble to turn there now, I'll copy some of it here as well.

Sound in a natural acoustic environment is reflected around the room. Size, shape, and surface treatments determine frequency response and nature of these reflections. A propagated sound passes through three stages:

- Direct sound
- Initial (early) reflections
- Reverberation

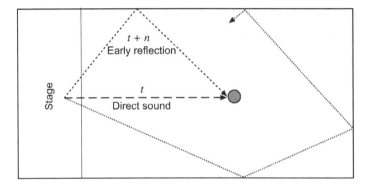

Direct sound is that experienced straight from the source, with no reflections from nearby surfaces affecting it. The closer you are to a sound source, the more direct sound you will hear.

Initial reflections are the first waves to be reflected from nearby surfaces such as walls, ceiling, floor, or room furnishings. They may or may not be heard as distinct echoes—it depends on delay time. The delay time before these early reflections becomes noticeable provides us with a sense of how large the room is. Longer initial delay = larger room. This is extremely useful when setting reverb units to recreate a particular sonic environment. If the delay between reflections is long enough, we hear distinct echoes. This occurs more in very large rooms (gyms, auditoriums) and outdoors.

The reflections in a room rapidly multiply, particularly when the sound source continues to produce sound. As reflections become more numerous, reflecting from all over the room, the result is reverberation. Here distinct echoes are no longer heard, but rather a wash of sound, referred to as the diffuse field.

Free Tip

There's an acoustic dividing line between this diffuse and direct sound, and you can actually hear it. Walk around a performance hall while an orchestra or somebody is rehearsing (don't do this during a real performance—people will stare). Walk slowly toward and away from the stage. Eventually you should be able to find a spot (roughly 1/4 or 1/3 of the way into the room from the stage area) where you can hear mostly reverberation if you lean back, but more direct sound from the stage when you lean forward. This boundary is termed the *reverberation radius*, and it turns out to be the ideal spot to locate your main stereo mic pair. Start here with your setup and then listen. If it sounds too close, move it back. If too reverberant, simply move it closer. This takes a lot of the guesswork away. If you are using omni-directional mics you'll want to locate them a little closer to the stage since they'll pick up more room reverberation from the back.

Another method is to put up two mics – one in the diffuse field, the other a little closer to the stage. Slowly move the second microphone closer to the stage while watching your meters; when you get a relative difference of 3dB between both mics, you've found the boundary. Use the same mics that you plan to record with.

Typical Large-Scale Hall Setup

If you're recording a fairly large source, such as an orchestra, concert band, or choir, follow these guidelines for selecting and positioning microphones so as to capture the entire group as faithfully as possible.

Main stereo pair

Choose between a coincident, near-coincident, spaced A-B, spaced A-B-C, or Decca Tree approach. All mics must be identical condenser-type models. This main stereo configuration should be located near the ensemble, not back in the hall as many novices tend to do. Place it relatively high, somewhat over the conductor's head, pointed down toward the middle or so of the ensemble.

Support mics

These are optional for soloists or other soft sources. Use large diaphragm condensers, positioned close to the source, and compensate their channels in the mix to ensure consistent panning, level, and time-of-arrival with the main stereo pair. For example, if the main mics are capturing this source over toward the right, you don't want the support mic to remain panned center in the recording— this smears that instrument between both positions.

Room mics

Place a stereo pair far back in the hall to capture ambiance and audience reaction. Typically a spaced A-B is used, though two boundary mics on the back wall work fine. The quality of the hall's acoustics will determine whether these are used or not. When using spaced A-B there are a couple things to keep in mind. Keep them several feet away from the walls (unless you're using PZMs), and less than 1/2 distance vertically between the floor and ceiling (to prevent standing waves).

With all of these mics, experiment with spacing and distances so as to capture an accurate, clean stereo image of the ensemble. If the instruments sound too scratchy or close, raise the mics a little. If you're getting too much hall reverb then you're too far away. A small change can make a huge difference. Some engineers might also add two omni-directional microphones on either side of the main stereo pair, closer to the ends of the ensemble. These provide additional depth and breadth from the group while adding some natural reverberation from the hall.

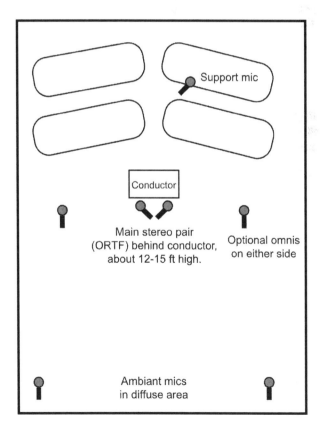

Typical Chamber Group Setup

As usual, begin with a primary stereo pair up front, not too far from the group. Actual height and distance depends on the nature of the room. Two additional omnis can be added as described above to add depth and ambiance. It's possible to individually mic each instrument, but this becomes more complicated for trying to get a natural mix from the group. By simply using a single stereo pair you let the ensemble control their own balance, which they should be able to do if they're good players. You also allow the total sound from the group to blend and mesh as it travels toward the mics. Close miking strings can be iffy at best, especially if you want a lush, thick string sound. We should also mention that it helps to record a chamber-style performance in a smaller room, thus mimicking the type of space these groups would use. The term chamber music comes from the days when small ensembles, such as string quartets, would perform in rich folks' living rooms. This is a very different sound than that of an orchestra blasting the 1812 through a large concert hall.

Listen for the blend between direct and diffuse (room) sound. If it sounds too close and in your face, move your mics back and/or higher. If it sounds distant and muddy, you probably want to move the mics closer. Chamber music is best reproduced fairly close, mimicking the environment of a small room.

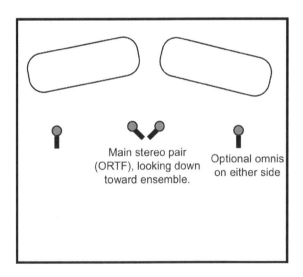

Main stereo pair (ORTF), looking down toward ensemble.

Optional omnis on either side

Stereo miking examples

The following audio examples demonstrate most of these stereo techniques with various distances from the source. Listen closely and you'll begin to distinguish the nuances in stereo width, perceived depth, and accuracy in reproducing the location of the players on stage.

Audio examples 110 - 115: Stereo miking techniques.

Mic setup descriptions for audio examples 110-115

#110: Neumann KM84, ORTF, 5' from stage, 6' high
#111: Neumann KM84, ORTF, 5' from stage, 9' high
#112: Neumann KM84, ORTF, 5' from stage, 9' high, Jecklin disk
#113: Neumann KM84, XY, 5' from stage, 9' high
#114: Neumann KM84, XY, 10' from stage, 9' high
#115: Neumann U87, Spaced pair, 5' from stage, 9' high

Chapter Thirteen

Understanding and Using the Equipment: Signal Processors – Frequency

Equalizer

An equalizer, or "EQ", is a circuit that changes the frequency response of a sound by boosting or cutting selected frequency bands. Think of it as a sophisticated tone control that allows you to make a sound brighter, less boomy, have more bass, and so on. To understand how it works, you first should get the concept of what actually makes sounds sound like they do.

There is a wide range of frequencies that are audible to humans—anything vibrating between 20Hz and 20kHz falls into our hearing range. All sounds coming from musical instruments, voices, or traffic on the highway produce a number of frequencies which fall somewhere within that band. What makes a trumpet sound different from a fog horn is the difference in *which* specific frequencies and *how much* of each frequency is included in that sound. In other words, the harmonic content of that sound is what makes it unique. We call this result the *timbre* of a sound.

With an EQ, we can actually raise or lower these frequencies within a sound— this alters the harmonic structure and therefore makes it sound different. You're not turning a flute into a guitar, but you can make that flute brighter by boosting the upper frequencies in that sound.

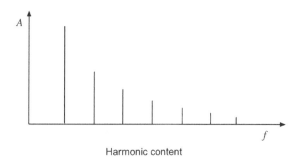

Harmonic content

Audio ex 119: 9dB boost at 4kHz   Audio ex 120: 9dB attenuation at 4kHz

Audio ex 121: 9dB boost at 8kHz   Audio ex 122: 9dB attenuation at 8kHz

Audio ex 123: 9dB boost @ 125Hz   Audio ex 124: 9dB atten @ 125Hz

Here's the difference between a high frequency peaking and shelving EQ. The first audio example is flat for a reference. The second is a peaking example to demonstrate a slight boost in the mid-range—it makes the guitar a little edgier. Now, the shelving EQ example has the same 3k boost point, but it boosts everything above that, so you hear all the tape hiss and other nasties way up there. In this case we would want the peaking EQ, but this will depend on the situation.

Audio example 125: Flat EQ setting (no change).

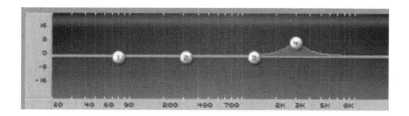

Audio example 126: Hi-EQ peaking boost, 3dB @ 3kHz

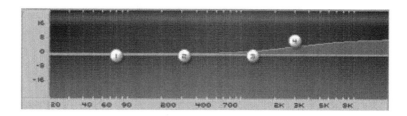

Audio example 127: Hi-EQ shelving boost, 3dB @ 3kHz

EQ suggestions and tips

- **To find a specific frequency**: Turn up the boost on a parametric EQ, then twirl the frequency select control until you find it.
- **Fix it BEFORE EQ:** Mic selection and placement is the key.
- **Boost less and cut more**: Humans are less likely to hear a cut, so this provides a more transparent approach.
- **Don't overdo EQ boost**: Try for 4-6 dB at the most.

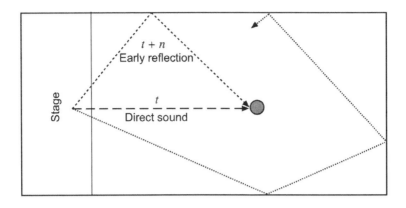

Delay Unit

A delay unit simply takes an incoming signal, holds it for a certain amount of time, then outputs it back to the console. In the really old days we used tape machines (a story for another day), but digital delays have been around for decades now. Digital units take an analog signal input, convert it to digital data, store the numbers in a buffer for the desired delay time, then output the data as an analog signal.

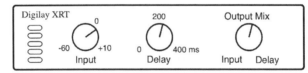

Digital Delay Unit

How do you plug it in?

Delay units are usually used as channel-specific devices. They can be plugged into the mixer using insert points to delay a single track, with the balance between original signal and delayed signal controlled on the delay device itself. They can also be routed with an aux send, with the return routed back to an empty channel on the board for balancing with the original signal from tape.

Application

Delay is useful for a number of things. One example is taking a single rhythm guitar track, running it through a delay unit, then panning the delay signal different from the original. The dual guitar track, when delayed, provides more depth to the part and the delay helps it move more in the mix.

Delay is also often used for vocals, whether in a subtle or more obvious manner. A subtle delay, with appropriate reverb and panning, provides greater sense of depth and fullness to a lead vocal. More obvious delays are for direct effect.

Doubling

You can make a signal sound fatter by generating another copy of it and delaying it very slightly. You won't hear the separate attack, but the double-attack thickens the sound just a bit.

Acoustic doubling

The best way is to have the musician(s) perform the track a second time and record this to another track; since no two performances will ever be identical this results in a thicker sound. Along with the minor timing differences (delay), this method also provides slight intonation differences which contribute to the effect.

Electronic doubling

Route a track through a digital delay, setting a very short delay time. It's not as rich as the acoustic doubling, but makes a big difference in the mix.

How do you plug it in?

Same as for delay units.

Application

Doubling can be used for nearly anything you wish to fatten. Very helpful for snare drum; this in conjunction with appropriate compression (longer release time) can really fatten and lengthen snare hits.

What's the difference between delay and doubling? Delay has a distinct separation between the initial signal and delayed echo. The time delay during doubling is so close we don't hear two distinct events, but rather a fused event which sounds fatter than the original.

Delays shorter than 15ms create comb filtering throughout the frequency spectrum. This is because different frequencies have different physical wavelengths, and if the time relationship is offset between two identical signals, the acoustical summing of the waveforms results in some frequency components getting louder, others softer. This alters the overall tone of the sound, so experiment with the delay settings to get a sound you're happy with.

> Audio examples 154 & 155: Adding delay to acoustic guitar, each example begins with no delay, then adds delay to the acoustic track.

> Audio examples 156 - 159: Adding delay to double an acoustic track. Each pair of examples compares no double/double.

> Audio examples 160 & 161: Adding delay to a bass guitar track.

> Audio examples 162 - 165: Adding delay to guitar track. Original is panned left, then add delay in right channel at 30ms, 60ms, 120ms.

> Audio examples 166 & 167: Processing a vocal in the mix, first dry, then w/ delay & verb.

Reverberation Unit

We always hear reverberation of some type and amount wherever we are. You've heard the difference between talking and singing in your living room, bathroom, and the school auditorium. Often in studio recording we try to eliminate or reduce reverberation in favor of a closer, drier signal. Then we can artificially add whatever we want for the final mix. Reverberation units take incoming signals and generate numerous reflections, simulating any particular environment you want. Over the years we've used these main types of units:

Spring

Ever hear someone drop a guitar amplifier and it went "sproing"? That's an example of a spring reverb, where an actual spring is connected to transducers. Feed a signal into the unit and it sends it flying back and forth along the spring, generating multiple reflections on the output. These aren't used much anymore, if at all, because they just don't work very well. I had to use a spring reverb many years ago, and every time the snare hit it overloaded the spring. Not very musical.

Plate

A plate reverb unit is a large metal plate suspended under tight tension. You set it up in the room, sound bounces against it, and the vibration of the plate generates reflections that are fed back into the console. Very cool, but too expensive these days for most facilities, especially since you can get much of the same effect from a digital processor.

Chamber

A chamber is a room, and some studios had a separate room dedicated to generating reverberation. The engineer would feed a track into the speakers mounted in the room; the sound would bounce around and be picked up by microphones that then fed this reverberant sound back to the console. This isn't done much these days because using a room exclusively for reverb is expensive and not really necessary due to digital processors that do such a great job.

Digital

Nearly everyone uses digital processors these days. These units take incoming signals and process them to output the desired effect, such as reverb, delay, or other special sounds. You can control lots of parameters to get it sounding just like you want, and then store this as a preset for later use.

Types of reverb patches (settings)

Halls

Hall patches reproduce the environment of an auditorium or other large space. Longer first reflections and denser, longer reverberation time are what make these sound distinctive.

Rooms / chambers

Smaller spaces are characterized by short first reflections and less reverberant sound. Think of a club or your living room.

Plates

Plate settings mimic the physical plate units described above. These typically sound brighter and crisper than hall or room settings.

Effects

Most processors not only generate reverb, but also produce lots of various effects. We'll describe a few of these a bit later.

User-set parameters

Reverb Time (RT60)

This represents how long it takes the reverberation to die away to a point 60dB below its original level. A large hall will have a longer RT60 than your living room.

Initial Delay

This determines when first reflections will be perceived and relates to how large we think the room is. So, set a longer initial delay time for a larger space. You can also make this extreme so you hear a distinct attack for effect.

Hi/Lo EQ

Most reverb units provide a simple EQ control so you can brighten or darken the reverberant sound.

Other settings

Some simple reverb units only provide a few settings, but others allow you to completely shape how the sound changes over time in a particular type of space. Play around with these various settings and see what you come up with.

Digital Reverb Unit

How do you plug it in?

Reverb units are usually not channel-specific devices. They can be plugged into the mixer for use on any number of channels through aux sends and returns.

For example, plug the aux 1 send to the reverb unit input, then patch the reverb unit output to any available aux return on the console. On each channel you wish to add reverb, simply turn up the aux 1 control knob. Remember signal flow? All these signals on the aux 1 bus combine at the master aux send 1, which you've routed to the reverb unit.

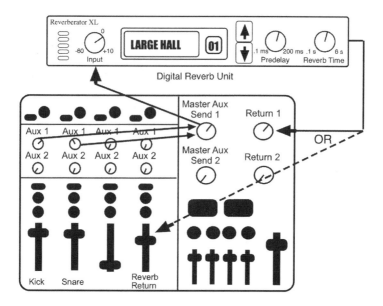

Application

Reverb is used for nearly any music recording project. Listen for different types of reverb patches to see which is more appropriate to the situation. You will often use more than one unit and patch setting in each song, such as putting a plate on the vocal and a large hall on the drums. Also carefully listen for reverb time—make sure the decay of the reverb matches the tempo and style of the song. Don't just settle for the factory patches—they're meant to be adjusted as needed.

Audio example 168: Small room reverb setting.

Audio example 169: Small hall reverb setting.

Audio example 170: Plate reverb setting.

> Audio example 171: Reverb with long RT (2.6s).

> Audio example 172: Reverb with short RT (1.0s).
> Audio example 173: Reverb with long pre-delay.

> Audio example 174: Reverb with gradually increasing pre-delay.

> Audio example 175: Reverb with tap delay.

Chorus

Ever thought about what makes a choir sound different from a solo singer? All those voices cannot sing exactly the same—there are slight differences in timing, timbre, and intonation. Aside from using a real choir, you can recreate this effect with a processor.

The chorus setting will take the incoming original signal and make a copy. The copy is delayed and detuned, then combined with the original. The result is a shimmering, fuller sound.

How do you plug it in?

Same as for delay units, either using aux sends and returns or inserting directly into a channel.

Application

Most of these effects can be applied to nearly anything, not just vocals. Learn to hear what the nuances are of each type of effect to determine what fits each particular situation. Chorus is useful for background vocal parts, guitars, keyboard pads, etc.

> Audio example 176 & 177: Chorus effect.

Flanging

Flanging occurs when a copy of a signal is continuously varied in time relationship with the original signal.

Huh? Run a track through a short delay, then constantly vary the delay time while listening to both signals. The combination of these two signals produces an ethereal sound quality. The term flanging came from the practice of having two identical tracks on two different tape machines—you start both at the same time, press on one machine's reel with your hand to slow it down, then release to let it speed back up. You're causing an extreme phasing relationship between both signals. Very cool.

How do you plug it in?

Same as for delay units, either using aux sends and returns or inserting directly into a channel.

Application

Flanging is very effective for guitars, vocals, drums, etc. It's a more pronounced effect than chorus. Try experimenting with either flanging or chorus to help keyboard patches such as organ come alive with more depth and movement. Send a keyboard track to the device, bring the flanged track back into a spare channel, add verb to both channels (so they both have similar ambiance), and pan apart. Remember to EQ similarly also.

> Audio examples 178 - 180: Flanging effect.

Phasing

Similar to flanging in the sound it produces, phasing uses very narrow bandwidth filters (remember the EQ chapter?) that are swept up and down the frequency spectrum. Two copies of the signal are used, one with the filter(s) sweeping up and down, the other not being affected. When combined, the filters create phase shift which cancels against the original signal. This cancellation affects different frequencies as the filter moves up and down, producing a very similar ethereal effect as flanging. Very popular and common for guitars.

> Audio example 181: Reverb with phaser.

Time Compression/Expansion

Sometimes you need to make a 62 second audio track fit into a 60 second slot. Digital processors allow us to lengthen or shorten an audio track without changing the pitch (to a certain extent).

Chapter Sixteen

Understanding and Using the Equipment:
Fundamental Sounds & Signals

The heart of all the information we've discussed in this text involves fundamental acoustics and electrical signals. Understanding these elements helps you better follow how we record sounds, route them through equipment, process them, and listen through speakers. Situations will arise in the studio and in live concerts where a solid understanding of acoustics and audio signals can help you determine possible causes and potential solutions. This chapter only attempts to get you started; there are many excellent books available that describe these concepts in greater detail.

Sound Waves

How do sounds actually get from one point to another? If you see someone flapping their mouth as they look at you, how does that covey anything meaningful such as speech? When we hear someone playing a musical instrument, how can we tell that it's a piano and not a snare drum? The answer lies in the vibration of air molecules—when an object vibrates, such as vocal cords, piano strings, or a saxophone reed, it changes the atmospheric pressure around it. These are relatively minor pressure changes—nothing like what happens when a hurricane comes through. But they are enough that when the vibration follows a particular pattern, it can convey information when received by our ears or by a microphone.

What's a pattern? Depends on the vibrating object. If it's a drumstick hitting a drum, then the sound pressure variations are fairly random and sound like noise to us. If it's a flute playing an A, then the sound waves follow a repetitive cycle—the particular waveform pattern of a flute repeats over and over until the playing stops. This is called a *periodic wave*, and all musical sounds feature this characteristic.

The sound itself is also distinguished by what the waveform looks like if you graph it out. Sound generated from a flute will set up a particular pattern of fluctuations different than that of a snare drum. These waveforms are built from simple sine waves—lots of them. You remember sine waves from geometry class, though you probably had no idea what they were used for. Now you have a practical application—sine waves, the most pure, simple form of vibration, combine in varying patterns to create complex sounds—instruments, noises, speech, etc. When these patterns repeat over and over you get a musical sound; when they are random you get noise.

A complex musical waveform

In audio equipment such as consoles and recorders, there is no physical object vibrating (except for a microphone diaphragm and a speaker cone). When an acoustic sound is transduced to an electrical signal with a microphone, the pressure variations then correspond to resulting changes in voltage. An increase in pressure equates to an increase in positive voltage, and a decrease in pressure is represented by negative voltage. Thus the electrical signal version is analogous to the original acoustic sound (thus the term *analog* in audio recording). This can be seen by graphing a simple sine wave—the positive curve going up represents the original acoustic pressure increase, and the curve going down into negative territory comes from an acoustic pressure decrease. This constantly fluctuates around the zero point, which is equilibrium (no signal), just as the AC voltage in your house constantly fluctuates between positive and negative. With audio signals, however, the fluctuation is much more complex and interesting compared to the plain 60Hz repetitive cycle in your power lines.

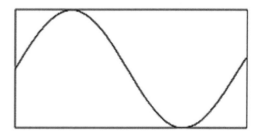

Simple sine wave where upward curve is positive voltage, down curve is negative.

As you probably know, these vibrating patterns must oscillate (vibrate) between 20 and 20,000 times per second to be heard by humans. This is known as *frequency*—number of cycles per second, which roughly equates to our sense of pitch (high or low). Translating this to musical terms, particular pitches are based on specific frequencies, such as the standard tuning note of A = 440Hz. A musical octave can be heard every time the frequency of a sound doubles, meaning that if you play a 40Hz tone, then double that to 80Hz, it will sound like the same pitch, only an octave higher. Audio equalizers are built with this in mind, where graphic EQs feature filters set at octave intervals, third-of-an-octave intervals, etc.

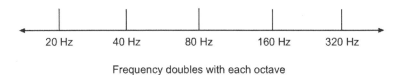

Frequency doubles with each octave

Different frequencies feature different *wavelengths*—low frequencies will have long waveforms (30 feet and longer) while higher frequencies possess much shorter waveforms. This is important when you consider issues of isolation in the studio, frequency response, and control of acoustics in a studio.

How much the variation moves from equilibrium (amount of pressure change) is referred to as *amplitude*. This is what gives us a sense of loudness, and in electrical signals running through your equipment it means how high or low your signal strength is. Moving a console fader up increases amplitude, moving it down decreases it. If a signal is too high in strength for a circuit it will distort; all audio equipment (including our ears) have a limited dynamic range, or capability of handling amplitude ranges. If a signal is too low, then you increase the amount of noise that is heard in the sound, so the engineer must balance signal levels pretty closely to get the best, cleanest sounding signal possible.

One more important concept for now—phase. Phase involves a time relationship for sound waves. Of particular interest in audio is when two identical, or nearly identical, soundwaves are shifted slightly in time from each other, then combined in a mixing console. Due to the normal algebraic summing of the wave components when you add two or more signals together, the varying positive and negative curves are now skewed somewhat and result in a different waveform. The difference depends on the amount of time shift which will affect different frequency components. The result? Your sound will change somewhat, usually resulting in a hollow, less-full sound. Why care about this? When you use more than one microphone at a time in the studio you run into phase issues. When you take a recorded track and process time delays and other effects you run into phase changes to your sound. When you set up for a live concert you must deal with phase relationships into your mics and in the hall due to wall/ceiling reflections. The most simple phase problem is when you wire your stereo speakers backwards on one side, or when a mic cable has been wired incorrectly. It's a big deal, it's difficult for novice engineers to comprehend, and it takes time to understand. Listen to your tracks as you record and see how it changes when you add that second mic to the mix—you'll eventually get the picture.

Characteristics of sound waves

Cycle

One complete sequence of a sound wave before it begins repeating itself. This refers to periodic waves, which are musical.

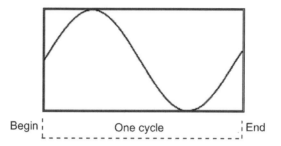

Amplitude

Vertical distance of the wave from center line (zero or equilibrium). Relates to perception of loudness, although it's not exactly the same thing.

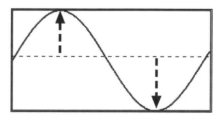

Amplitude from equilibrium

Frequency

Number of cycles completed per second (Bandwidth). Relates to, but not the same as pitch. The audio bandwidth that humans can hear is between 20Hz - 20kHz, lower on the high end as your hearing deteriorates over time. Keep in mind that this frequency range is only a small portion of the entire radio spectrum that includes radio, tv, microwave, etc.

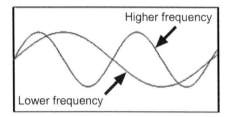

Wavelength

Physical length of the sound wave from one point in the cycle to the next identical point. Notice how the diagram looks identical to that of *cycle*. The difference is that cycle is measured in time and wavelength is a physical length. Low frequencies are longer (up to and greater than 30 feet) while higher frequencies become progressively shorter.

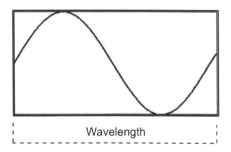

Phase

Measured in degrees (360° = full cycle)

Phase shift - time delay between two identical waves. Anything other than 0 or 180 will affect the sound by altering the harmonic structure.

Phase cancellation - 180° phase shift which results in total cancellation of both waves

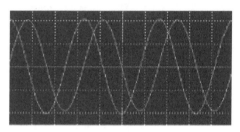

Phase shift

Harmonic content

All sound waves are made of a particular combination of sine wave components (harmonics).

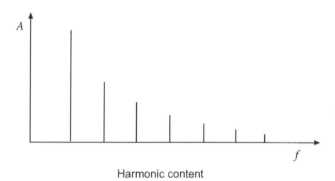

Harmonic content

Harmonics make sounds distinctive

Number and relative strengths of individual sine waves comprise a sound and determines tonality or timbre.

- *Fundamental* - lowest frequency in a complex wave. Determines basic pitch of the note.
- *Overtones / Partials* - higher frequencies in complex waves.
- *Harmonics* - overtones which are multiples of the fundamental.
- *Timbre* - perceived tone quality based on harmonic content. Identifies trumpet sounds from flutes, etc.
- *Noise* - contains all frequencies and has irregular waveform.

How exactly do sine waves add up to something more interesting than a test tone?

Here is a single sine wave (test tone):

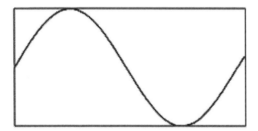

Next, we'll add a second sine wave at twice the frequency of the first. The graph below shows both individual waves.

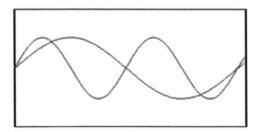

What happens when these two waves are combined? This results in a complex wave that does not look like a sine wave anymore. It also begins to have a more interesting sound, though it has a long way to go to sound like music and other noises that we hear. The darker wave in the graph represents the resulting complex wave.

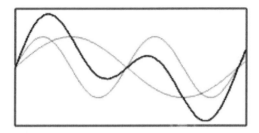

Finally, we've added a great many sine waves that, at certain frequencies and amplitudes, add up to a square wave (the dark line). This can be intentional as when using a synthesizer to reproduce a certain sound, or it can be a problem such as when you overdrive an amplifier or recording medium. When this happens, the original waveform has a higher signal level than the system can handle, so the extreme high and low amplitudes are chopped off (clipping). The result is a bunch of new sine wave components that weren't in the original sound, and are now altering the sound in an unpleasant way (distortion).

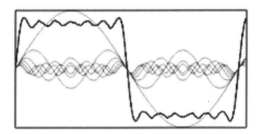

Here is an audio example of a waveform that was recorded too high, clipping the system. You can see the flattened top and bottom, which resembles the square wave described earlier.

Why is this important?

Knowing frequency content of various instruments helps with setting EQ. It also helps you during mic selection—if a sound has mainly low frequencies (kick drum), then you need a mic that can adequately capture and reproduce that range. Understanding the issues of overdriving audio systems can help identify and prevent unwanted distortion.

Other basic acoustics concepts

Envelope

All sounds have a volume shape over time—how the sound rises and decays away. We can alter this with dynamics processors (compressors and gates), and we control it when we use synthesizers to reproduce or create sounds. A percussion hit will have a very rapid attack and quick release, while a violin has a more gradual volume envelope. An organ has an instantaneous on, fairly steady sustain, then immediate release when you take your finger off the key.

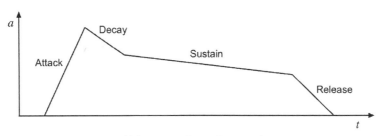

Volume envelope of a sound

Velocity of Sound in Air

The speed of sound is different in various materials or mediums. We most often are concerned with how fast sound travels in air, though studio architectural design requires knowledge of how fast sound can be transmitted through various building materials. Live reinforcement engineers have to work around time delays between sound coming from the main speakers and from on stage; they can calculate how long it will take for the original sound on stage to reach the audience, then program in specific delays into the loudspeaker system to compensate. Here's a comparison of sound velocity in different materials.

- Air: 1087 ft/sec at 32°F (344 m/s) – dependent upon temperature (+/- 1 ft/sec per $^{\circ}$F change)
- Water: 1433 m/s
- Glass: 3962 m/s
- Steel: 5029 m/s

Reflection, Diffraction, and Diffusion

Within a room, sound waves will reflect from surfaces. The nature of the room surfaces as well as the frequencies involved will determine how much waves will reflect as opposed to being absorbed by that surface. Compare the difference in sound between a bathroom, which usually has very hard surfaces such as tile, and a living room that is filled with soft objects such as furniture, plants, carpet (and people). The bathroom is much more lively and reverberant. Selection of materials and construction techniques are crucial for controlling the acoustics in a studio, concert hall, etc.

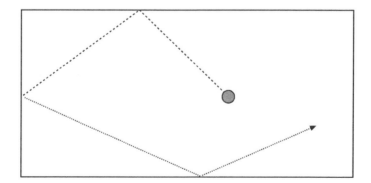

Hard surfaces will reflect sound energy until it eventually dies away.

Sound also bends around objects, more so in the low frequency range. This is how you can hear your neighbor's bass guitar down the hall, but not the high hat and cymbals. Sometime when you're bored and need some cheap entertainment, stand in front of a speaker, then move off to one side. The high frequencies will diminish, but the lows will stay solid. This can be a problem in the studio when trying to isolate instruments from each other during recording—bass frequencies will travel all over the room and leak into the microphones. It's also an issue when mounting and locating monitor speakers in the control room. Different placements in the room and around the equipment will give you very different sound responses. It's these invisible characteristics of sound that are so problematic for people trying to set up their own studios—they do not understand what's really happening with their sound, and therefore their recordings suffer accordingly.

Notice how the sound changes after you begin furnishing an empty room? Part of this is a change in reflections as described earlier, but it is also due to changes in the wall and floor surfaces. When you hang pictures and tapestries on the walls and install bookshelves you create an irregular wall surface that scatters sound waves. This is a good thing, and we even employ specially-built units called *diffusers* to do this in a more efficient way in the studio. It provides a more well-rounded ambiance, preserving a sense of liveness in your recording room that we need for music to sound natural.

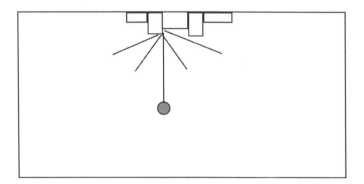

When sound energy hits an uneven surface, it scatters
back into the room more evenly.

Human Hearing

We won't get into a complicated discussion about how the brain deciphers sounds transduced by your ears. For now we'll focus on a few key aspects you should be aware of when working in the studio.

The main concept is that human hearing is non-linear. This means that you don't hear what you think you are hearing. In other words, there are various issues involved in how we perceive sounds. For instance, if you double the wattage of a power amplifier, you would assume that the volume would double. Not so. The actual perceived increase is only 3 dB—barely noticeable. It takes 10 times as much amplification to make it sound twice as loud. Remember studying logarithms in school? This is where it comes into play, where changes in loudness (and pitch) is logarithmic and not linear. Later in this chapter we'll briefly introduce you to decibels and using logarithms to calculate various sound and signal levels—don't freak out, it'll be okay.

There are also differences in sound depending on how loud we listen. If you listen at lower volumes, then you hear less bass and treble frequencies. If you crank it up very loud, you will hear much more bass and treble than usual. If you engineer your recordings based on these listening levels, then they will sound quite different when played back in various situations. There is a graph that shows us how this works (Fletcher-Munson), and the suggested solution is to listen at about 85 dB SPL. How would you find this? Go purchase a $50 SPL meter at Radio Shack or an iPhone app that measures sound levels.

One other issue to remember is that our ears can be "overloaded" with excessive volume. Not only will this cause permanent hearing loss over time, but there are immediate implications as well. Your ears will quickly tire and lose perspective the longer you work. If you quit for the day and come back later, you'll notice how different your recordings sound. Engineers should take breaks regularly during long sessions. If you listen to very loud levels for any extended period of time, you will also begin to hear distortion at some point, but this is actually happening in your own hearing system. The concept is exactly the same as what happens when you overload a power amplifier (or any audio component). The signal hits maximum dynamic range and any level over that point gets clipped. This essentially creates a square wave, adding a host of unrelated sine components. The resulting waveform is different and adds noise that is usually unwanted and unpleasant. Our ears do the same thing. Early in my career I was working with a producer who liked to monitor at really high volumes. It wasn't long before I was hearing distortion in the monitors, but it wasn't from any signal levels I had running through the console. It took a moment to realize it was all in my head, so to speak, but in a very real way. Knowing I had set everything up okay before this kicked in allowed me to complete the session without worrying about what was being recorded, but it was a weird experience.

Perception of Direction

The chapter on stereo microphone technique discussed briefly how humans hear direction of sound. Using differences in amplitude and time of arrival between left and right, we can tell where sound sources are located. This is also used to create a sense of direction when mixing in the studio. Pan potentiometers and digital delays follow these two principles when placing images in various stereophonic locations. Different stereo miking techniques follow these principles in capturing a sense of stereo space from the stage source.

Perception of Space

Humans get a sense of the room they are listening in through such cues as direct sounds and reflections. This was described in the chapter on time-based processors. Once a sound is generated, the listener will hear the direct sound straight from the source, then begin to detect early and late reflections from nearby surfaces. These are not distinct echoes, but very closely-spaced reflections in the millisecond range. The longer it takes for the brain to detect an initial reflection after hearing the original direct sound, the larger the room is perceived to be. We can therefore use time-based processors to create any type or size room for a particular recording.

Audio Signals (Electrical)

What is an audio signal?

We can take an acoustic sound wave and convert (transduce) it into an analogous electrical signal. Microphones take care of this function, and then we can route these signals through mixing consoles, signal processors, and recorders. Eventually these signals will be converted again into acoustic waves so we can hear them through monitors. The point is that the basic principles we discussed for acoustic waves apply the same to signals—it's the same audio information, only conveyed in a different transmission medium.

With this in mind, you now know that audio signals possess characteristics of frequency, amplitude, phase, etc. These are very important concepts to understand when working with audio. Again, read a good text that explains in-depth the nuts and bolts of audio signal theory. For now, we'll provide just a few examples of why you should pay attention to this stuff.

Wonder why old recordings seem to lack that luster and clarity of newer recordings? Older recording equipment lacked the frequency response of modern technology, meaning higher and lower frequencies on either end of the audio spectrum simply could not be captured and reproduced. Most obvious is the standard "telephone" sound, which we now mimic as a vocal effect by rolling off the highs and lows, leaving only the mid-range. Knowing the frequency ranges of various instruments and voices helps you to better find EQ settings that fit that particular part. We select different microphones for certain miking situations based on their individual frequency response and sound—they're intentionally made to sound unique. So, you'd most likely put a large-diaphragm mic on a kick drum but not on a flute in order to match that instrument's low-end frequency range.

Signal amplitude refers to how much juice is flowing through your circuits. Over-drive your microphone preamp and it'll distort. Crank up too much EQ and you can overload the EQ circuits. Record too hot on your recorder and it'll distort. If you set signal levels too low, however, you get a lot more noise added to your sound. Connect a piece of gear into another that's not matched correctly and you'll have problems getting the levels to work. Notice some equipment that has a level change switch on the back, say between +4 and -10 or -20? That's there for a good reason, and you need to know which level your overall studio is running so you can purchase and connect equipment that will work correctly.

We've mentioned phase issues that exist acoustically when you use multiple mics in a room, and the results show up when mixing those signals on the console. The most common situation is miking a drum set. When you're recording a drum set and have several mics running at once, start listening to one mic at a time, gradually building the drum mix. At some point you might notice that the kick, snare, or something thins out. You just added a mic that's in adverse phase relationship with the mic on that particular instrument. Either move one of the mics a little (might not take much), or try flipping the phase button on one of the mic channels on the console. Use your ears, and some consoles provide a phase indicator as well to help you out.

We can run into phase problems electronically as well. Take a track, double it while adding a short delay, then pan together and listen for how the sound thins somewhat (depending on delay time). I once took a student's mix to a local radio station for the program director to consider playing. It was a really interesting, different type of record, and they decided to play it. But the only available playback unit the guy had was a mono (one speaker) boombox, so we sat nervously through the intro hoping the vocal wouldn't cancel out completely due to the stereo effects he had added. This is why you always do a mono compatibility check on your mixes just in case someone might not have a stereo unit...pretty rare these days, thankfully. You can also run into electronic phase problems with incorrectly wired cables. For example, mic cables have three wires inside, two for signal and one for ground. The two signal wires must be connected to the correct pins, and if these are reversed at one end of the cable you've got a complete 180 degree phase shift. That's a problem, so you should check your cables with a cable tester to be sure.

Another example:

Measured sound pressure level = .075 dynes/cm^2
Reference level = .0002 dynes/cm^2

dB SPL = 20 log .075/.0002

dB SPL = 51.5

Here's how to tell the dB increase with your new guitar amplifier:

Original guitar amp was 50 watts

New guitar amp you got for your birthday is 100 watts

dB = 10 log 100/50

dB increase = 3.01

Note that with wattage (power) measurements the formula uses 10 log, whereas with voltage and sound pressure measurements 20 log is used. This is true for both acoustic and electrical calculations.

Audio reference levels

There are two most common reference levels for audio gear. What this means is that when you see your console meter showing 0dB, the actual signal level running through your circuits varies significantly depending on which standard your equipment was designed for. Professional gear provides higher signal levels due to higher quality components, resulting in a better sound overall.

- Professional: +4dBu = 1.23 volts based on a 0.775 volt 0dBu reference
- Semi-Pro: -10dBu = 0.316 volts based on a 1 volt reference

Know which level your gear is operating so you can interface them together properly. Pay attention to those level switches on the back of your devices—they match either one of these references, and you need to have the correct setting to interface these units together.

Tools to measure SPL and signal level

Meters on the console or recorder

We've mentioned audio meters from time to time. There are two primary types, and they provide a visual indication of signal level. However, they operate quite differently and will affect your recording decisions accordingly.

- VU (Volume Unit). These have the little needle that swings over toward the right. VUs provide an averaged value that corresponds to our perception of volume. It will not show all the peaks and dips, the same as the fact that our ears don't register very brief bursts of signal (transients). You can overload something without realizing it, so consoles typically also provide peak LED indicators that will flash when you're pushing close to the danger zone.

- Peak Reading. These are usually step graph indicators or simple LEDs. They are designed to respond to any instantaneous signal change, and will therefore show all peaks and dips in levels. Sometimes they will also feature a "peak hold" function, meaning it will keep the highest indicator lit for a little longer so you don't miss any transients along the way.

VU   Peak

Sound pressure level meter

SPL meters measure acoustic sound pressure levels as described earlier in this chapter. They actually measure the changes in pressure using dynes/cm^2, then convert this to a decibel reading that makes sense to engineers. They're pretty easy to use, but you have to understand the weighting network system to use them properly.

If you read up on Fletcher-Munson curves, you'll know that this graph shows us that we hear lows, mids, and highs differently at different volumes. To get an accurate reading on an SPL meter, you must adjust the internal weighting network for the general volume level you will be running in your situation.

These are referred to as A, B, and C weights with the following applicable SPL levels:

A: Referenced to 40 Phons (levels of 40 dB or lower)
B: Referenced to 70 Phons (levels in the 70 dB range)
C: Referenced to 100 Phons (levels of 100 dB or high

Other audio meters

There are several other devices used to measure audio for various applications. Standard multimeters can be used to directly measure voltage, current, or resistance in an audio circuit. Specialized audio tools can measure dB comparisons, frequency response, noise levels, impedance, etc. These can range from $10 for a cheap multimeter to several thousand dollars for high quality audio maintenance equipment. With the advent of iPhone apps, several companies have developed pretty good audio tools that run on your phone, and they're very affordable. They use either the built-in mic or an external mic to capture sound and provide the same processing and analysis you find with hardware tools. You can then save the results and email them to your client. Amazing stuff.

About the author

Dr. Barry R. Hill is professor of music and director of the Music Recording Technology Degree Program at Lebanon Valley College in Pennsylvania. A member of the National Academy of Recording Arts and Sciences and the Audio Engineering Society, he has extensive experience in the industry as a recording engineer, consultant, conference panelist, workshop presenter, and performer. Dr. Hill's academic teaching areas include recording production, music licensing and contracts, copyright law, and learning psychology. As director of the college's Center for Excellence in Teaching and Learning, he also applies his expertise and research in learning psychology to help faculty and K-12 music teachers improve their classroom teaching and better understand the learning process.

Dr. Hill holds degrees in Instructional Design from The Pennsylvania State University, Music Technology and Interactive Media from New York University, and Music with Recording Arts from the University of North Carolina Asheville.